SOCIAL CAPITAL
AND HEALTH

SOCIAL CAPITAL AND HEALTH

Catherine Campbell
Gender Institute, London School of Economics

with Rachael Wood
Gender Institute, London School of Economics
and Moira Kelly
Health Education Authority

Acknowledgements

We would like to thank the following people who have taken the time to provide information, comment and advice at different stages of this project.

The study was initiated by Pamela Gillies, Director of Research at the HEA. Other members of the HEA/LSE project advisory team were Antony Morgan, Robert Leonardi, and Dominic McVey.

A research liaison group was set up to share information about the study with members of the 'Healthy Luton' group (which has now become the Luton Health Action Zone) and included: Sue Chirico, Brenda Sainsbury, Paul Barton, Maria Parocki, Julie Higgs, Lynda Bleeze, Leena Jones, Gurch Randhawa, Jenny Amery, Gail Findlay and Bhagwant Sagoo.

Valuable comments on an earlier draft of this report were provided by Mel Bartley, Trevor Hancock, Ray Pahl, Virginia Morrow and Nick Doyle.

Additionally we would like to thank: Rhiannon Barker, Henrietta Moore, Hazel Johnstone, Anne Green, David Owen, Christine Callum, and Rhiannon Walters.

The report was written by Catherine Campbell, a social psychologist at the London School of Economics (LSE). Rachael Wood, a research officer at the LSE Gender Institute, and Moira Kelly (of the HEA) contributed significantly to the development and management of the research, as well as to the data collection process.

ISBN 0 7521 1659 2
© Health Education Authority, 1999
Health Education Authority
Trevelyan House
30 Great Peter Street
London SW1P 2HW
Printed in Great Britain

Contents

Acknowledgements   iv

Social capital for health Preface to the series   vii

Executive summary   ix

Introduction   1

1. The relevance of social capital to health promotion   7

2. Social capital in local communities in England:
   the Luton pilot study   30

3. Setting the context: perceptions of social capital
   in Farley and Sundon Park   33

4. Trust and local identity: the quality of community
   relationships in the past and present   68

5. Civic engagement 1: Informal networks of friends
   and neighbours   102

6. Civic engagement 2: Voluntary networks linked to
   leisure, hobbies and personal development   118

7. Civic engagement 3: Local activist networks and
    perceived citizen-power   134

8. Conclusion   153

References   158

Appendices   163
A In-depth interview informants   163
B Interview topic guide   165
C NUD*ST coding frame: categories for analysis of   169
    in-depth interviews

Social capital for health
Preface to the series

The recently published Acheson Report on Inequalities in Health and the Government's public health strategy 'Our Healthier Nation', recognise that the solutions to major public health problems such as heart disease, cancers, mental health and accidents are complex. They will require interventions which cut across sectors to take account of the broader social, cultural, economic, political and physical environments which shape people's experiences of health and wellbeing.

A major challenge is how to influence these broader determinants of health in such a way that relative inequalities in health can be addressed.

Recent evidence suggests that social approaches to the organisation and delivery of public health may have considerable potential for health improvement, particularly for those that suffer most disadvantage in society. The evidence base for moving forward in this field is, however, somewhat limited.

The Health Education Authority is committed to developing this evidence base and to testing social approaches to reducing health inequalities and to the promotion of health and the prevention of disease.

The HEA's first Research Strategy 1996–99 initiated a programme to investigate the concept of social capital and to establish the empirical links between aspects of social capital such as trust, reciprocity, local democracy, citizenship, civic engagement, social relationships, social support, and health outcomes, access to services, information and to power.

Social capital serves as one coherent construct which will allow us to progress the debate and discussion about the general importance of social approaches to public health and health promotion. It is however only one part of an approach to health improvement, which must also clearly embrace structural changes.

The HEA's new programme of Social Action Research in two city sites will build upon the evidence produced thus far, to demonstrate the effectiveness of a range of integrated social approaches, implemented through collaborative initiatives by local authorities, health authorities and the voluntary sector.

The early work on social capital will also feed into new in-depth analyses of social networks and citizen power and their importance to health by gender, age, ethnicity and further explore its relationships to health and inequality in individuals and in populations.

Over the coming year the HEA will be publishing a series of reports summarising the initial results of the exploratory work on social capital and its links to health.

This report presents detailed findings from a qualitative study of social capital and health carried out in England. It highlights a number of important issues for contemporary health promotion, in particular the importance of informal networks to connect people to each other and improve access to health-related information and services.

Professor Pamela Gillies
Director of Research
Health Education Authority

Executive summary

What is a 'healthy community'?

Within health promotion there is currently an emphasis on community action – with health promoters aiming not only for individual behaviour change, but also for the development of community contexts which enable and support healthy behaviours.

It is important that those seeking to promote health-enabling communities have a realistic understanding of the types of community networks, resources and relationships that exist in their local communities of interest, and that their understandings of community resonate with the experiences and perceptions of ordinary people at the grassroots level. However, our understandings of what constitutes a 'health-enabling community' are still in their infancy.

This report examines the possibility that Putnam's (1993) concept of 'social capital' might serve as a framework for the design and evaluation of community-level health promotional interventions and policies and for research into the health-community interface.

Social capital

Putnam defines social capital in terms of four characteristics:
- the existence of *community networks*
- *civic engagement* (participation in these community networks)
- local *identity* and a sense of solidarity and equality with other community members
- norms of *trust* and *reciprocal help and support*.

A great deal of research has pointed to links between social capital and a range of positive political and economic outcomes. More recently it has been argued that social capital might also be associated with positive health outcomes.

Structure of the report

Literature review

The first section of the report discusses existing methods of health promotion (including information-based approaches, peer education, community-led participatory approaches and public health movements), as well as current theoretical debates about factors that influence health at the individual, community and macro-social levels of analysis. It illustrates ways in which the concept of social capital has the potential to fill gaps in our understandings of the determinants of health-related behaviours, and of the mechanisms underlying the success or failure of health promotional interventions.

The empirical study

Using in-depth interviews and focus groups, the empirical study examines community networks and relationships in ward-level local communities in England. It focuses on two less affluent wards in the city of Luton – one characterised by relatively low levels of health and the second by relatively high levels of health, in the interests of exploring whether levels of social capital might be higher in the 'high health' ward.

Two aspects of social capital (trust and civic engagement/perceived citizen power) appeared to be higher in the 'high health' community, and two aspects (local identity and local community facilities) higher in the 'low health' community. The implications of these findings are discussed. It is argued that certain aspects of social capital might be more health-enhancing than others, and that much research remains to be done in following up this exploratory finding.

The report provides a micro-qualitative account of people's involvement in a range of social networks: informal face-to-face networks of friends, neighbours and relatives; voluntary associations related to leisure, hobbies and personal development; and formal and informal community activist groups and initiatives. Those relationships of trust and reciprocity that did exist in our communities of interest were located overwhelmingly within informal face-to-face networks of friends, neighbours and relatives, and the report highlights the relatively minimal role played by other network types in our informants' lives. Attention is given to those aspects of contemporary working and living conditions that limit the development of the more generalised forms of community-level trust and local identity and reciprocal help and support pre-supposed by Putnam's characterisation of social capital.

There was evidence for strong within-community differences in the way in which social capital is created, sustained and accessed, and the report emphasises the need for more attention to the interaction of social capital, gender, age, socio-economic status and ethnicity. It is concluded that the notion of social capital has the potential to make a valuable contribution to our understandings of what constitutes a 'health-enabling community', and seven recommendations for further development of the concept are put forward.

Introduction

The HEA's research

The Health Education Authority (HEA) is committed to commissioning research and evaluation which will advance understanding of the way in which social and life skills approaches can contribute to the public's health in terms of the promotion of health and prevention of disease. The HEA is particularly concerned to apply the findings from research in efforts to tackle inequalities in the experience of health and well-being in England.

Recent policy documents such as the Acheson Report on Inequalities in Health (Acheson, 1998) have drawn attention to social inequalities and the effects that they have on health status. Acheson details a number of recommendations for the reduction of health inequalities. The wide ranging nature of the recommendations makes it clear that solutions to major public health problems like heart disease, cancers, mental ill health and accidents are complex, and involve social, environmental and economic, as well as biological and psychological factors.

Understandings of the mechanisms which mediate between, for example, poverty and poor health, are still in their infancy, and the issues involved here are extremely complex (Popay *et al.*, 1998). Clearly there are many such mediating mechanisms. Gillies *et al.* (1996) suggest that one of the mechanisms through which factors such as poverty, discrimination and deprivation might exert their negative influence on health is through the role that they play in undermining stocks of health-enhancing social capital in deprived communities.

This report presents the results of one important exploratory research project which set out to assess the notion of social capital and its links to health. Lessons learned from this and other related projects will feed into an expanding evidence base which will inform a new HEA demonstration study, the Social Action Research Project.

The influence of social factors on health

There is considerable evidence to show that social factors influence health, and this is reviewed in detail in Chapter 2. The focus of this study is on exploring how social factors impact on health. Factors closely associated with health include social support, integration or isolation, social networks, social roles and activities (Blaxter, 1990). For example, research by Berkman and Syme (1979) has shown that factors such as social isolation may have wide-reaching health consequences. They found lack of social and community ties to be associated with increased risk of mortality. Given such evidence, theoretical models are required which will enable the research findings to be linked with policy and practice.

The concept of social capital was proposed as a potential way of explaining how community-level factors may influence health. As such, it was considered to have potential for providing the basis for a conceptual model which could lead to the development of new social (capital) indicators. These indicators would be used to evaluate interventions which aim to increase the impact of certain social factors which have been found to be beneficial to health (e.g. social cohesion), and reduce the effects of those which have been found to be negative (e.g. social exclusion). The 'social capital indicators' would complement those that are used to measure the effects of other factors on health, including the physical environment, for example housing and transport.

Social capital

The most well-known proponent of social capital is probably Putnam, a political scientist who used it as a theoretical concept to explain findings from a 20-year study of regional government in Italy (1993). He equates social capital with civic community, describing it as features of social organisation, such as trust, norms, and networks, which work to improve the health, wealth and industry of a community. Trust, which is developed through norms of reciprocity and networks of civic engagement, is seen as an essential feature of social capital. In this sense people will perform activities which will benefit others with no immediate reward, knowing that this will ultimately benefit them or their families. They will also take an active part in how their local community is organised. We decided to see whether social capital as described by Putnam could be of value in relation to health promotion in the UK. The overall aim of our research was to develop increased understanding of the relationship between social capital and health and consider how this knowledge could be applied through national and local policy initiatives to promote public health.

Public health policy

There is an emphasis in recent UK government policy on inter-agency working, collaboration, partnership, and community participation to a much greater extent than previously. This is evident in the public health strategy paper, *Our Healthier Nation* (Department of Health, 1998), and in related documents such as *The New NHS* (Department of Health, 1998), and *Modern Local Government* (Department of Environment, Transport and the Regions, 1998). A number of initiatives directed at improving health have arisen from these policy frameworks, for example, Health Improvement Programmes, Health Action Zones, Primary Care Groups, Healthy Living Centres, and Health Impact Assessments.

As well as policy and practice initiatives, which set out to address health directly, interventions that may affect the health of individuals and communities more indirectly are now also acknowledged as important (see Acheson, 1998). For instance, strategies such as the Crime and Disorder Act (1998) through its emphasis on community safety can be seen to contribute to the determinants of health, as fear of crime may lead to stress, which in turn influences health. A feature of recent strategy frameworks is that community participation, local democracy, social networks, and prioritisation of need at local level, are key tools identified in producing change. This is exemplified in programmes such as the 'New Deal for Communities' which will provide funds to develop and implement local community-based plans covering a wide range of areas, including jobs, crime, housing and health (Social Exclusion Unit, 1998).

Against this policy backdrop we can start to see the beginnings of a shift in the locus of health promotion, from the individual to the community. Whereas it is the social context that is important, the place at which interventions are often targeted and evaluated will be the 'community'. It is acknowledged that 'community' may take many forms. Programmes which have aimed to educate individuals about healthy lifestyles, such as giving up smoking, and being more physically active are still seen as important, and the need for good public health information is stated in *Our Healthier Nation* (OHN). However, it is recognised that such programmes have limitations and tend to work best with those whose social circumstances are more favourable, i.e. the better off (for example, see Marsh and McKay, 1994; Gillies, 1998). It is argued, therefore, that effective approaches, which take into account the social context in which people live, work and play will need to be developed. Public health policy emphasises the need to take social factors into account. This can be seen in OHN:

> 'When social problems – poor housing, unemployment or low pay, fear of crime and isolation – are combined, as they often are, then people's health can suffer

disproportionately. Social exclusion involves not only social but also economic and psychological isolation. Although people may know what affects their health, their hardship and isolation mean that it is often difficult to act on what they know. The best way to make a start on helping them live healthier lives is to provide help and support to enable them to participate in society, and to help them improve their own economic and social circumstances. That will help to improve their health.'   (p. 17)

Health promotion programmes aimed at communities are not new, but have to some extent taken a back seat compared to those aimed at changing the health related knowledge, attitudes and behaviours of individuals. It can also be argued that much community development work that is not formally aimed at improving health will have an indirect effect on health outcomes. For example, local authorities are setting up initiatives to promote the 'economic, social and environmental well-being of their area' (Department of the Environment, Transport and the Regions, 1998). One apparent reason for the relatively low prominence of community-based health promotion, is the dearth of useful health promotion models that take into account the social determinants of health, and there is consequently a lack of good published programme evaluations.

In relation to the 'Healthy Cities' programme, Hancock (1993) comments that although considerable efforts are made in communities to improve health, research and evaluation have tended to lag behind. Certainly in the UK, although there is considerable research to show that social factors do influence health, there have been relatively few published studies of attempts to turn the findings into policy and practice. This means that a lot of the lessons to be learned are shared in a relatively ad hoc way by different teams initiating (and evaluating) action. Consequently, the evidential basis for improving health through community-based initiatives is currently limited.

A key challenge for those involved in public health is to develop useful models, and related to this evaluation frameworks for social action programmes (in communities) to promote health. This should introduce ways of doing systematic evaluations, making comparison between areas possible. For example, if a particular intervention is used in the same way in more than one community and appears to be effective when assessed by reference to the same set of indicators, it would make generalisation of the findings (to other communities) possible. At the same time, evaluation frameworks need to be flexible to allow 'communities' to tailor programmes and evaluations to reflect their own particular economic, social, and cultural needs. A particular need is for good indicators that can be used at local level to assess the success of community health promotion programmes. These may include initiatives such as those mentioned above, for example Health Action Zones.

Social capital is one of a number of models which may be a useful tool in the development of community level health promotion research, policy and practice. It has received a great deal of attention in a number of disciplines over the last few years. Its popularity appears to lie in part in its capacity for engaging inter-disciplinary debate around social policy issues. It is of interest to academics, policy makers, and practitioners, and can provide a common language for dialogue between these groups (though not necessarily agreement on its characteristics, effects and implications for policy). It has also attracted attention throughout the world, in both developed and undeveloped countries. We suggest that it has the capacity to provide a valuable link between theory and practice, the absence of which people working to develop practicable local policy often lament. In this sense, it may support the development of new theoretical frameworks for health promotion activity, with particular attention paid to the development of policy and appropriate indicators for measuring the effect of action, at both national and local levels.*

This qualitative study

Despite an ever-growing literature on social capital in relation to a wide variety of topics such as economic policy and education, relatively little empirical research has as yet been reported, in particular on the relationship between social capital and health. The qualitative research described here is a parallel study to that by Leonardi *et al.* (in preparation), who has conducted a pilot survey based on the original questionnaire used in the regional government in Italy by Putnam, Leonardi and Nanetti (1993). Given the lack of empirical work on social capital in relation to health specific to the UK, qualitative research was required to explore whether or not levels of social capital vary in communities that have comparable socio-economic status but vary in terms of levels of health. It also aimed to examine the extent to which Putnam's characterisation of social capital needs to be developed or reworked in the light of a number of important differences between the contextual location of his work and the current study.

The research findings highlight a number of important issues regarding future planning and evaluation of community health promotion initiatives. These are discussed in the Conclusion. We believe that this research makes an important contribution to the on-going task of developing clearer conceptualisations and indicators of social capital in this country, and hope that as our understandings of social capital develop, the concept will play an increasingly important role in future explorations of the mechanisms whereby social inequalities exert their negative effects on health. However, before research can focus on the important question of potential poverty–social capital–health relationships,

*The development of appropriate indicators for use at local level is a complex task and will require considerable work. However, this research can be used (alongside other research) to contribute to the formulation of indicators.

we need to have a clear understanding of what constitutes social capital – how it can best be conceptualised and measured by health researchers in local communities in England. Ultimately, we hope that research of this nature will contribute to policy debates on how best to reduce inequalities, by providing greater insights into the mechanisms through which social factors influence health.

In sum, this is an exploratory case study which aims to be of value to those working to develop health promotion theory, practice and research methodologies. It provides empirical findings, which can provide a basis for theoretical debate on social capital and health, appropriate to the UK. It can also contribute to the development of appropriate social indicators for the evaluation of programmes aimed at communities. This complements current research programmes developed by the HEA and other organisations aimed at improving health.

Moira Kelly
Research Manager
Health Education Authority

1. The relevance of social capital to health promotion

Health educators are often criticised for unrealistic optimism about the potential of their educational interventions to promote health-enhancing behaviour change – in the absence of back-up policies and programmes that seek to promote community contexts likely to enable or support desired behaviour change. Understandings of those aspects of community life which are 'enabling' of health-enhancing behaviours are still in their infancy however. This chapter examines the possibility that Putnam's controversial notion of 'social capital' – developed in the context of the disciplines of political science and economics – might serve as a useful conceptual tool for exploring the relationship between health and community-level networks and relationships.

The details of Putnam's work are widely available (for example Putnam, 1993a, 1993b, 1995) and extensively reviewed elsewhere (for example Harriss, 1997; Gillies, 1998; Leonardi, 1997; Morrow, 1998; Portes, 1998), so they will only be summarised briefly here. Social capital refers to the community cohesion that results when a community is characterised by a rich associational life – a variable array of strong social networks, all of which collectively constitute what he refers to as the 'civic community'. Putnam defines social capital in terms of a number of characteristics. These include the existence of *community networks* which together constitute the civic community (involving institutions, associated facilities and relationships) in the voluntary, state and personal spheres, and the density of the networking between these three spheres; *civic engagement* or participation in the process of sustaining and/or using such voluntary, state and interpersonal networks; *civic identity*, referring to people's sense of 'belonging' to the civic community, together with a sense of solidarity and equality with other community members; and norms governing the functioning of networks, in particular norms of co-operation, *reciprocity* (obligation to help others; confidence that others will help oneself) and *trust* (as opposed to fear) of others in the community.

Levels of social capital have been found to be associated with a range of positive political and economic outcomes in contexts as diverse as Italy (for example Putnam, 1993a) and Tanzania (for example Narayan and Pritchett, 1997). Most of the social capital research in the Putnam (1993a) tradition falls within the disciplinary boundaries of economics and political science. More recently a range of authors (for example Gillies, Tolley and Wolstenholme, 1996; Gillies and Spray, 1997; Gillies, 1998; Kreuter, Lezin and Koplan, 1997; Lomas, 1998) have argued that social capital might also be associated with positive health outcomes, and suggested that Putnam's concept might usefully be imported into the field of health promotion. In this chapter we seek to emphasise that in making such calls, care must be taken not to 'reinvent the wheel'. An extensive literature already exists in the sociology and social psychology of health regarding the relationship between social relations and health. This chapter examines the extent to which insights offered by the concept of social capital resonate with work that has already been done by health researchers, and examines whether the concept might fill a gap in our understandings of community-level influences on health.

Existing approaches to health education

Information-based health education programmes

Historically the bulk of health education efforts have favoured the provision of information – often by health experts – to passive target audiences, by means of posters, pamphlets, school lessons and radio and television programmes. Such educational messages rest on a range of social psychological models which suggest that individual rational choice is a key determinant of health-related behaviour. If one supplies rational individuals with information about health risks, they will behave in ways that minimise such risks (this view being based on the assumption that people always act in ways that maximise their interests). Thus, for example, if one informs individuals that smoking increases their risk of lung cancer and heart disease, and persuades them that lung cancer and heart disease are undesirable outcomes, then target audience members will smoke less, or hopefully stop smoking altogether. This assumption is reflected in the ubiquitous 'KABP model' which assumes that health-related *Practices* are a function of individual *Knowledge*, *Attitudes* and *Beliefs*. Various forms of 'KABP-type' thinking exist, enshrined in theories such as the Health Belief Model (Janz and Becker, 1984), the Theory of Reasoned Action (Fishbein and Ajzen, 1975), the Theory of Planned Behaviour (Ajzen, 1988) and the Transtheoretical Model (Prochaska *et al.*, 1994). While such theories always refer to the influence of broader social and cultural contexts on behaviour, social context is generally conceptualised as a static backdrop in a way that is difficult to operationalise in concrete health promotion interventions. Little attention has been paid to developing detailed understandings of the types of social networks and relationships that constitute the social context of which such authors speak.

Over the years, however, much evidence has suggested that contrary to the KABP assumptions, people often knowingly indulge in behaviour that places their health at risk (for example Gatherer, 1979; Gillies, Tolley and Wolstenholme, 1996; Kippax and Crawford, 1993; Wilton and Aggleton, 1991). Despite knowing about potential health dangers, people continue to have unprotected sex with multiple partners, to smoke, to drink too much, to overexpose themselves to the sun, to eat high-salt and high-fat diets. This presents a challenge for health educators. If knowledge and individual choice are only partial determinants of health behaviour, what are the other determinants?

Alternative approaches: peer education programmes

Against this background there has been a call for health educationists to review the models they use in planning and evaluating their work. One such call has involved expanding the individualistic and cognitive emphasis of social psychological KABP-type models, and locating the process of behaviour change at the level of the peer group rather than the individual. Against this background, there have been some innovative attempts to develop alternative approaches to health education, including methods falling under the broad heading of 'peer education'. These programmes move away from the KABP approaches which view knowledge and attitudes as the primary determinants of behaviour, taking account of the insight that perceived social norms are also important influences on behaviour. People are more likely to change their behaviour if they perceive that liked and trusted peers are changing theirs (Social Diffusion Theory, Rogers, 1983). Another important theoretical influence here is Social Learning Theory (Bandura, 1986) which states that peer modelling is an important process in shaping behaviour.

On the basis of such insights, attempts have been made to implement programmes where health-related information is disseminated by members of target peer groups. 'Peers' might be scholars, or members of sports clubs or religious groups. More ambitious peer education projects have been attempted with 'hard-to-reach' groups such as homeless people or injecting drug users or sex workers. While Du Bois-Reymond and Ravesloot (1994) emphasise that a great deal of research remains to be done into the extent and nature of the role played by peers in shaping and constraining behaviour, studies in a number of countries have pointed to the success of peer education as a behaviour change mechanism in programmes ranging from sexual health to smoking (Dube and Wilson,

1996; Kelly *et al.*, 1991; DiClemente, 1993a, 1993b; Mellanby *et al.*, 1995; Klein, Sondag and Drolet, 1994; Wiist and Snider, 1991).

Another theoretical influence in designing and explaining peer education processes has been the concept of *self-efficacy*, referring to the degree to which a person feels in control over important aspects of his or her life (Bandura, 1977). The greater one's sense of self-efficacy, the more likely one is to engage in health-promoting behaviours (Bandura, 1996). There are a range of ways in which peer education programmes can potentially enhance participants' subjective sense of self-efficacy. Ideally, target group members need to be involved in designing and planning such educational programmes; conducting the formative research and social mapping necessary to identify the range of peer groups in the area of concern; doing the necessary outreach work to contact their peers; initiating the debate and discussion of the particular health-related behaviours that are the central core of the programme (Dube and Wilson, 1997). Clearly this level of participation is limited to a smaller number of leading 'peer' figures in the programme. However, well-designed programmes should also provide opportunities for increased self-efficacy among all participants, insofar as participants should ideally play an active role in the debates, discussions and role plays that form the core of peer educational interventions. To cite an example from the field of sexual health, Aggleton (1994) outlines four key activities that should be included in sexual risk reduction programmes of the peer education variety: provision of information; activities that encourage personal risk appraisal; training in sexual negotiation skills (especially how to refuse unsafe sex); and provision of resources (both in terms of access to health services and to condoms). Each of these activities has the potential to lead to higher levels of self-efficacy amongst intervention participants. Increased self-efficacy should also result from a demystification and 'de-professionalisation' of medical knowledge, insofar as the responsibility for health promotion is taken out of the hands and discourses of 'experts' and put into the hands and into the discourses of ordinary people.

Problems with peer-education approaches: need for theoretical development

While peer education programmes have been successful in some countries and contexts, there is no consensus regarding the value of this approach. This is the case in England, for example, where it is common for health professionals to dismiss them, simply saying that they do not work. Others argue that disappointing results of many peer education programmes might be because attempts to implement them have not always been guided by sound theoretical understandings of the mechanisms of behaviour change, or of the way that health-related behaviours are shaped and constrained by the broader social and community contexts within which peer groups are located. Each of these points will now be discussed in turn. Milburn (1995) argues that one of the reasons for the patchy achievements of peer education must be traced to an inadequate understanding of the processes underlying the success or failure of such programmes, in particular the processes underlying the dissemination of information in networks and groups. 'Peer education suffers from an inadequately specified theoretical base, which does not address the important social and cultural factors implicit in the approach' (Milburn, 1995, p. 418).

While the potential success of peer education programmes would clearly depend on those psychological processes detailed in theories of Social Learning, Social Diffusion and Self-efficacy referred to above, it is argued here that these approaches need to be located within the broader context of a social psychological approach which accommodates not only the intra-individual and inter-individual levels of analysis (as these approaches tend to do), but also seeks to locate these intra-individual and inter-individual processes within the context of broader community and social relations. Campbell (1998) suggests that the concept of social identity provides a potentially useful mediating link between the insights provided by these theories and the social/community level of analysis. Drawing on the work of Stockdale and colleagues (1989, 1995), she argues that peer education programmes succeed or fail in enhancing the processes of social learning, social diffusion or self-efficacy to the extent that they resonate with the social identities of target audiences. She outlines the link between social identities and health in a number of points:

> Point 1: Social identities play a key role in the performance of health-related behaviours. Our identities consist of a series of frequently shifting affiliations with a series of loosely defined group memberships (e.g. family, peers, community members). Different group memberships are associated with a range of socially negotiated recipes for living (discourses and practices) which shape and constrain experience and behaviour, including those experiences and behaviours that are relevant to health.
> Point 2: In the process of constructing identities, people are motivated by a fundamental human need for positive self-esteem, self-efficacy and empowerment. (Campbell, 1998)

This emphasis on the interlocking processes of identification and self-efficacy/ empowerment resonates with insights from a range of sources. These include:
- the social capital literature with its emphasis on the role played by community identity and active civic engagement in delivering a range of positive social outcomes;
- the radical health promotion literature with its focus on the development of critical consciousness, which consists of a common identity between participants in health promotion networks, and which serves as a resource empowering people to take action against the social conditions that undermine their health (for example Freire, 1973); and

- the community health literature with its emphasis on the existence of a sense of community identity as a key factor motivating or empowering people to participate in community-based health projects (Rissel, 1994).

Point 2 will be take up again below, where the processes of self-esteem, self-efficacy and empowerment will be cited as important psycho-social pathways mediating between community resources and health. At this stage we focus chiefly on the social identity framework – which would explain the success of peer education programmes in bringing about behaviour change not simply because they set off the types of behaviouristic modelling mechanisms detailed in, for example, Social Learning Theory, or because they enhance particular psycho-social mechanisms such as self-efficacy, but because they provide a context in which members of groups who are vulnerable to particular health risks are given space to actively refashion their social identities in a collective way through discussion and debate with like-minded peers (rather than changing behaviour because an 'expert' has told them to). Norms of health-related behaviours are cultural and social products, constantly constructed and reconstructed at the peer group level, and involving the active engagement and participation of peer group members.

This emphasis on active group members collectively constructing and reconstructing health-related norms and behaviours is consistent with the growing literature that seeks to view high-risk health behaviours *not* in terms of rational individual decisions based on knowledge or information – *but rather* as reflections of the cultural and social norms of particular groupings with common social identities (Stockdale, 1995).

Against this background, how might we begin to develop more precise characterisations and operationalisations of the broader social contexts within which peer groups negotiate health-related social norms? While existing social psychological theories of behaviour change frequently assert that behaviour change takes place within particular social and community contexts, few of them go very far in detailing exactly which aspects of social and community context are important.

Gillies' model provides a starting point for this task (Gillies, 1996).

In terms of Gillies' 'onion-model', individual health is shaped and constrained by factors at a number of analytical levels. It is argued here that one of the reasons why peer education programmes might not have been successful as hoped in the United Kingdom is because they seek to influence behaviour at the levels of 'individuals' and 'peers', and fail to take account of the location of peer groups within 'communities', 'social institutions' and 'systems of culture, politics, economics, and environment'.

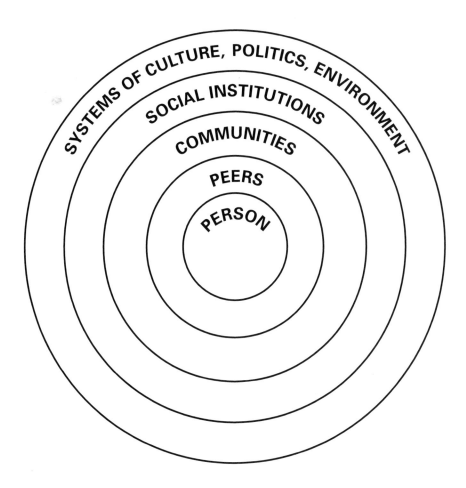

Gillies' 'onion-model' of influences on individual health

In the light of Gillies' model, while peer education programmes have the potential to alter health-relevant cultures in a limited and local way – amongst target group members, and those in their immediate peer groups – the extent to which they succeed in transforming the broader community and social contexts which contribute to the performance of high-risk behaviours in the first place is an open question. Some (for example Schoepf, 1993) argue that peer processes *do* form the basis for broader social and cultural changes. Others (for example Asthana and Oostvogels, 1996; Stone, 1992) argue that peer processes cannot be successful without simultaneous and consistent changes in the institutional, political, economic and legal structures within which individuals and their peer groups are located. This resonates with the claim made by Putnam and others in the social capital literature, who suggest that for social capital to have optimally positive effects, there needs to be dense networking between the personal, voluntary and state dimensions of social life.

The effects of peer education programmes may often not be generalisable beyond the immediate communities of the particular peer group members involved in interventions. Along these lines, one might claim that this approach works with a rather narrow notion of self-efficacy – confining this process to the individual and peer group level, and failing to take account of the broader range of social and economic processes that limit people's ability to shape their health-related behaviour.

This leads to the importance of adding a third point to the conceptualisation of identity outlined above:

> Point 3: Social identities are negotiated within the particular community, social, economic and cultural contexts in which people live and work. These contexts often determine the extent to which people have access to opportunities for empowerment/self-efficacy. Here empowerment must be regarded as both a subjective state (referring to the subjective sense that one is in control of important aspects of one's life) as well as an objective state (given that a range of social, political and economic factors will constrain the extent to which one is indeed in control of important aspects of one's life or not).

Thus, many would argue that the peer education approach is guilty of unrealistic optimism about the potential of such programmes to work without the back-up of broader policy approaches which promote the development of environments that support the behaviour changes the education programme seeks to bring about. However, the development of such broader policy approaches presupposes an understanding of those aspects of community and social life which are 'enabling' in relation to health. It is here that the social capital approach could make an important contribution – through pinpointing the types of community networks and community relationships that enhance health.

As critiques of traditional educational approaches gain ever wider acceptance within health education circles, there is a shift in discourse, where people are speaking less and less of 'health education' and 'behaviour change' and more and more of 'structural interventions' and 'enabling approaches'. Tawil, Verster and O'Reilly (1995) define enabling approaches as those that try and create circumstances that *enable* behaviour change to occur rather than trying to *persuade* people to change their behaviour. Such approaches focus on the social and political factors that facilitate or impede behavioural choice, and they aim to remove structural barriers to health-protective action as well as constructing barriers to risk-taking. Tawil and colleagues illustrate their argument by discussing the context of HIV transmission in developing countries. They argue that enabling approaches should focus on the economic development of at-risk groupings, as well as on development policy. In their view, the crucial issue at stake in HIV transmission in their countries of interest is the powerlessness of many women to protect themselves against HIV infection in the face of male reluctance to use condoms. They discuss a number of economic and policy strategies aimed at improving women's access to resources and reducing their financial dependence on male partners. The discourse of 'enabling approaches' represents an important shift in health educational thinking.

While few would disagree with the substance of the argument of Tawil and colleagues, their analysis illustrates a common tendency to polarise health promotion possibilities in terms of micro-social individual behaviour-change mechanisms on the one hand (for example the use of condoms by individuals), and macro-social structural and economic interventions on the other hand (for example the economic empowerment of women). Concepts such as social capital, which focus on formal and informal networks at the local community level of analysis, represent an important intermediary stage between the micro-social individual and the macro-social levels favoured in such polarisations.

Community participation health programmes in developing countries

Brief attention is given to attempts to establish more ambitious community participation health education projects in developing countries. Several of these projects rest on sounder theoretical foundations than similar projects in developed countries, insofar as they have explicitly tried to promote the development of enabling environments for health education. However they too have faced many problems, and provide a number of useful lessons for those concerned with understanding the interface between social relations and health in a way that can inform the design of community-based health promotion projects as well as health policy.

Community participation approaches refer to the proliferation of projects following the 1978 World Health Organization Alma-Ata conference, which pledged commitment to encouraging community participation in the planning, implementation and management of health projects in developing countries. Such projects have generally involved peer educators and support groups, but in addition to this have aimed to take account of the wider social, cultural and economic factors associated with health-damaging behaviours. They have gone hand in hand with the proliferation of non-governmental organisations which aim to empower members of groups particularly vulnerable to particular health problems, working at the local level in projects which aim for 'community ownership' as their highest goal.

Despite the high hopes held out for community participation, community-based health projects have often not been successful, and a growing number of articles try to analyse the reason for the gap between the rhetoric and reality of community participation as a health promotion strategy (for example Madan, 1987; Asthana and Oostvogels, 1996; Stone, 1992). Many of the problems highlighted in these reports echo problems that have been faced by those attempting to develop community participatory health projects in the UK with 'hard-to-reach' groups such as injecting drug users and commercial sex workers (for example Rhodes, 1994a, 1994b).

Asthana and Oostvogels (1996) point out that most so-called 'community participation' programmes are established around priorities shaped in a top-down way by health educators, rather than growing out of the 'felt needs' of the target group. The fact that priorities are often imposed on community groups in a 'top-down' way, undermines the aim of such programmes to increase people's sense of self-efficacy through grassroots project ownership. This highlights the issue of what is meant by 'participation' in health programmes. Madan (1987) emphasises that the participation of target communities in health-related projects can take a number of forms – ranging from the ideal situation where a community initiates a health project, and seeks assistance from health professionals in resourcing and implementing it (genuine participation) to the other end of the spectrum where health professionals initiate a project and persuade community members to participate (participation based at best on co-operation and at worst on obedience). According to Madan, greater conceptual clarity needs to be gained regarding different forms of participation; why participation is such an important goal; by what mechanisms participation should achieve its desired effects and so on. The concept of social capital – with its emphasis on the role of civic engagement/participation in the generation of a wide range of community benefits – provides an interesting point of entry into the examination of such issues.

Another important issue in the developing world literature relates to whether or not community cohesion and civic identity (that is social capital) can be created, or to what extent health promoters are limited to identifying and working with already existing social networks and resources. Some argue that community-based health-related projects are most likely to succeed when they work with already existing social networks (Ankrah, 1993). The failure of several UK-based community outreach projects has been attributed to programme organisers' mistaken assumptions about the existence of particular target communities (for example male sex workers, or youth groups) – in situations where in fact these alleged 'communities' did not constitute homogeneous identity groups as assumed by the organisers (Rhodes 1994a, 1994b). Often people assumed by health educators to constitute a community (for example intravenous drug users) turn out to be a heterogeneous group, rather than a peer group characterised by a common identity – which would bind informants together in the task of renegotiating behavioural norms and practices. Social interaction and solidarity do not automatically flow from neighbourhood proximity, or from the fact of addiction to a common substance, as many programme organisers have so optimistically assumed.

Referring to community health promotion in the US, Israel *et al.* (1994) suggest that health educators should take care to identify and work in contexts which already show some existing sense of community. Where this is not possible, they argue that the primary task of a health programme should be to try and strengthen latent community possibilities by attempting to develop a sense of communality among the target group for the health intervention. In a similar vein Eisen (1994) highlights the importance of community organisation and capacity building as prerequisites for successful health programmes. In the UK also, bodies such as the National AIDS Trust (1995) are increasingly pointing to the importance of a community capacity-building phase prior to the implementation of health promotional programmes in 'hard-to-reach' communities. This involves a careful process of community mapping, the identification of community groups which have the potential to conduct health promotional work (both in terms of a potential sense of communality, and in terms of the potential to develop organisational skills), and an intensive phase of organisational development in these groups to maximise their potential for conducting health promotional work. Much more work needs to be done in developing understandings and actionable models of what constitute the 'communities' whose existence is presupposed by so many health educational interventions.

An important aspect of Putnam's concept of social capital is the existence of dense horizontal networks of formal and informal community networks. This insight echoes a growing constituency among health promotion workers in both developed and developing countries who are emphasising the importance of 'alliances' or 'partnerships' among different community 'stakeholders' as an important component of successful community development. Thus, for example, HIV prevention workers in the UK are increasingly emphasising the importance of 'shared responsibilities' for community health – embodied in the development of partnerships between players in the statutory, voluntary and community sectors in health promotional work.

In a pioneering review, one of the few published studies which begins to explore possible links between health and social capital, Gillies (1998) points to two factors which have repeatedly been cited as key markers of 'best practice' in successful health promotion projects in a range of countries and contexts. The first of these is local community involvement in setting agendas for health promotional action (a point which has already been emphasised above). The second factor she refers to is that of the effectiveness of alliances or partnership initiatives to promote health across sectors, across professional and lay boundaries and between public, private and non-governmental agencies. She argues that such alliances provide potential contexts for tackling the broader determinants of health and wellbeing in a sustainable manner, as well as giving comprehensive support to efforts to promote health-related behaviour change. As Gillies says, the concept of social capital, with its emphasis on community co-ordination, co-operation and reciprocity, provides a potentially useful starting point for conceptualising the types of social networks, and the nature of interactions between them, which are most likely to lead to health-enabling community contexts.

In short, much work remains to be done in developing a comprehensive framework that will pull together existing knowledge about community networks, community identities, participation and health-related behaviours. The concept of social capital provides a useful starting point for this task. Much work remains to be done in converting the concept of social capital from a descriptive model to an explanatory theory but, as we argue below, existing work in the social psychology and sociology of health provides a number of conceptual tools for this task.

Public health movements: Healthy Cities

Moving away from health education to the broader field of health promotion and public health, the Healthy Cities Movement (HCM) is gaining momentum through its efforts to enhance and build health-promoting networks and practices in a number of cities throughout Europe. Advocates of the HCM (Davies and Kelly, 1993) hail the approach as a reaction to the stranglehold of the biomedical model that dominated the practice of public health in Europe between 1930 and 1970. They see the HCM as part of a challenge to the biomedical approach to health in the light of (i) growing concern at the endless resources that were being eaten up by high technology modern tertiary medical care; and (ii) an objection to a health educational approach whose basis was derived uncritically from social psychology and epidemiology, aiming to change individual lifestyles, while ignoring the wider community, environmental and socioeconomic factors shaping health. Hancock outlines the fundamental presuppositions of the HCM in his 'multi-factorial' model of health determinants, 'incorporating both physical and social environmental determinants from the individual level to that of our culture and global ecosystem' (1993, p. 17). Building on the insights prompted by the World Health Organization's 1978 Alma-Ata declaration, the 1986 WHO Healthy Cities movement was based on the insights that the promotion of health must include the adaptation and transformation of those social structures that foster ill health, and that community participation is the most powerful method of attaining this goal. Healthy Cities attempt to maximise involvement of a wide range of community representatives in health promotion, backed up by the development of appropriate health policies at both the local and national levels.

Despite the fact that the HCM appears to have generated a great deal of activity across a wide range of countries and contexts, advocates of the approach bemoan the lack of appropriate research techniques and concepts to document and evaluate the processes underlying the approach (Hancock, 1993). If hard research evidence can be gathered to demonstrate a link between health and social capital, the concept could be developed into a useful set of indicators of some of the processes which the HCM seeks to stimulate. Many of the health-promoting social relations which the HCM seeks to foster – strong local government, broad community ownership, effective committees, strong community participation, intersectoral collaboration and political and managerial accountability (see Tsouros, 1990 for a more extensive list) – could be usefully operationalised within the social capital framework.

Existing work linking social capital to health

Social capital has already become something of a buzzword in development and social policy circles, but as yet little systematic attention has been paid to it in the field of health, and few researchers have taken up the task of explicitly operationalising the concept in the interests of (i) formally establishing whether there is a direct link between health and social capital; and (ii) defining the concept in a way that is useful for action and policy in the area of health promotion. Gillies, Tolley and Wolstenholme (1996) highlight the importance of these goals in their suggestion that the concept of social capital has an important role to play in understanding the mediating links between HIV/AIDS and poverty. They detail some of the mechanisms whereby poverty facilitates HIV/AIDS transmission, including factors such as homelessness, limited educational opportunities, the low status of women and the disintegration of neighbourhoods. Factors such as these interact to destroy the social cohesion of communities (that is social capital), increasing the vulnerability of community members to health problems. Projects aiming to promote health in deprived communities need to focus not only on economic development to solve the problem of poverty, but also simultaneously on the development of social capital or what Gillies and colleagues refer to as the process of 'network enhancement', that is the promotion of those health-enabling social structures which are weakened or undermined by poverty. Economic regeneration needs to be accompanied by social regeneration. Furthermore, indicators need to be developed to measure the success of community development health promotion initiatives which go beyond measuring individually focused biomedical and behavioural outcomes, and focus also on the extent to which projects have succeeded in generating the social capital which is, they argue, an important prerequisite for sustaining the health gains that such projects seek to achieve.

Gillies, Tolley and Wolstenholme (1996) emphasise that it is not clear whether the concept of social capital is relevant to the contexts of developing countries. This comment echoes the work of Wilkinson (1996), another researcher who has explicitly drawn links between social capital and health in his book *Unhealthy societies: the afflictions of inequality*. The concept of social capital serves as a major explanatory construct in Wilkinson's work on the relationship between health and social inequalities in developed countries, where he argues that health and quality of life in modern societies is primarily dependent on the interlocking factors of distributional justice and levels of social capital. He argues that amongst developed countries, it is not the richest countries that have the best health, but those with the smallest income differences. Health is related to relative rather than absolute income levels. The reason for this is that egalitarian societies are more socially cohesive, they have a stronger community life. The public arena becomes a source of supportive and health-promoting social networks rather than a source of stress, conflict and ill health.

For Wilkinson (1996), egalitarian societies are much more supportive of their members, who are thus much healthier. The lower the income differences in a society, the more supportive the environment, the less stressed its citizens and the higher the levels of health they experience. Egalitarian societies have more social capital than unequal ones. They are characterised by higher levels of trust amongst their citizens. They are more socially cohesive. They have stronger community life and suffer fewer of the corrosive social effects of inequality. The public arena becomes a source of supportive social networks rather than a source of stress and potential conflict. On the other hand, social inequality increases crime rates and violence, undermines the likelihood of densely overlapping horizontal social networks, and imposes a psychological burden which reduces the wellbeing of the whole society.

Wilkinson argues that these principles are only likely to hold in countries that have achieved the level of wealth necessary to make the 'epidemiological transition' – where the main causes of death have changed from infectious diseases (as is still the case in poorer countries, and as was the case in the early history of now-industrialised countries like Britain) to degenerative diseases. Wilkinson suggests that the health-enhancing benefits of social capital presuppose a particular level of economic affluence.

Authors such as Gillies, Tolley and Wolstenholme (1996) and Wilkinson (1996) allude to the future potential of the concept of social capital in understanding the causes of health and ill health, and in designing and evaluating more effective health promotion campaigns and policies. In the sources cited above however, neither of them goes very far in explicitly operationalising the concept of social capital for health research. This task is more explicitly addressed by Kreuter, Lezin and Koplan (1997), who outline a research project currently in progress in the US. This project uses the notion of social capital as a means of evaluating a series of public health projects which aim to provide the social and political contexts in which community-based health promotion projects are most likely to succeed. Kreuter, Lezin and Koplan justify their interest in the light of three starting assumptions: (i) theoretically sound health promotion interventions and tactics will be effective to the extent that the target community has organisational entities and systems that are supportive of the enterprise, and that these entities and systems are activated; (ii) the activation of relevant community entities and systems depends in part on the extent to which community members are aware of, value and trust the proposed intervention; and (iii) because notions of activated organisational entities and community trust are fundamental constructs of social capital theory, measures of social capital might reveal important insights into questions of intervention feasibility, timing, effectiveness and so on.

They conceptualise social capital as a relational term that connotes interactions between people through systems that enhance and support that interaction – a specific set of processes among people and organisations working collaboratively in an atmosphere of trust, that leads to the accomplishment of the goal of mutual social benefit. Civic engagement is regarded as the critical component of successful community-based health promotion interventions. In concrete terms the PATCH (Planned Approach to Community Health) programmes seek to train state health education leaders to work with local-level counterparts in establishing community health promotion programmes that mobilise a strong core of representative local support and participation. Kreuter, Lezin and Koplan (1997) outline a research project which seeks to examine their hypothesis that there will be a high correlation between achievement in the PATCH programmes (measured in terms of planning, leadership, fidelity and standards, support, outcomes and sustainability) and levels of social capital in the relevant communities. This project will seek to measure social capital in terms of both (i) community and organisational level activity (voter turnout, newspaper readership, volunteerism and so on) and (ii) what they call 'individual measures' (in particular individual perceptions of trust, reciprocity and civic engagement). Kreuter and colleagues provide a useful range of detailed guidelines on how one might begin to design survey items that measure the latter component of social capital.

Factors mediating between health and social relations

Despite the high expectations that the concept of social capital is generating in health promotion and policy circles, the concept is not without limitations. It is argued here that at its current state of development, social capital has the status of a descriptive construct rather than an explanatory theory – leaving room for further development if the concept is to contribute to our understanding of the pathways between social relations and health. The poor explanatory power of the construct of social capital in Putnam's 'home discipline' of political science has been highlighted by Levi (1996). She argues that Putnam has, as yet, failed to explicate the mechanisms whereby high levels of involvement in voluntary associations and networks (and the allegedly associated relationships of trust, reciprocal help and support) lead to more effective local government. Ironically while this problem is such an acute one in Putnam's home discipline which seeks to link social capital to good government, this is not the case when we import the idea of social capital into the area of health promotion, where a large research literature already provides a range of starting points for developing hypotheses about the pathways between community networks and relations on the one hand, and health on the other. This literature postulates relationships between health and social relations at the individual, inter-individual, organisational, community and macro-social levels of analysis. While it is useful to isolate these levels of analysis for analytical purposes, the interactions between the levels are manifold.

Self-efficacy

At the *individual* level of analysis, a large research literature documents links between levels of *self-efficacy* (as defined by Bandura, 1977, 1996) and health. Self-efficacy has already been defined above as the degree to which a person feels in control over important aspects of his or her life. Self-efficacy is believed to have an impact on health in two ways. Firstly it affects the likelihood that people will engage in health-enhancing behaviour. The greater one's sense of perceived control, the more likely one is to engage in behaviours that are known to affect one's health status. Secondly levels of self-efficacy affect people's stress levels. Low levels of perceived self-efficacy may lead to anxiety and stress, and have an impact on health through a range of health-damaging stress-related behaviours and biological processes (discussed below).

Similar concepts which have been found to correlate with health status include *internal locus of control* (Strickland, 1978), *perceived behavioural control* (Ajzen, 1988) and *sense of coherence* (Antonovsky, 1984, 1987). It is speculated here that high levels of social capital will serve to increase people's sense of self-efficacy and/or sense of coherence such that they are more likely to engage in health-promoting behaviours, and less likely to suffer the damaging behavioural and biological consequences of stress and anxiety.

Social support and social networks

At the *inter-individual* level we have concepts such as *social support* and *social networks*. The health of individuals is related to the extent to which they are located within strong and supportive social relationships. The extent to which individuals are integrated into their communities is predictive of a generalised range of disease outcomes (Berkman, 1995). Population-based research over a twenty-year period suggests that people who are socially isolated are at increased mortality risk from a number of causes. The inter-related concepts of social support and social networks have been developed to explain these results. Many studies have testified to the positive correlation between levels of social support and the likelihood of engaging in health-promoting behaviours (Cohen and Syme, 1984; Gottlieb, 1981). *Social support* is a feature of *social networks* (groupings based on family membership, friendship, neighbourhood and community contacts and so on). According to social network research, the individual and others in his/her social networks represent an interdependent and dynamic system, where the individual's health depends not only on his or her behaviour and social situation, but on the interlocking behaviours and social situations of others in the network (Berkman, 1995). For social support to be health promoting, it must provide individuals with a sense of belonging and intimacy. It must also help people to be more competent and self-efficacious. A myriad of definitions of social support exist, distinguishing between its objective/actual and subjective/perceived dimensions, and looking at the different forms that social support takes (for example emotional, instrumental, financial). In addition to a range of direct practical benefits resulting from social support, it is also said to serve as a buffer against stress. Historically there has been an emphasis on the health-enhancing benefits of *receiving* social support. Of late, an interesting new literature is beginning to develop on the health-enhancing benefits of *giving* social support.

Despite the fact that an almost infinitely large research literature exists on the relationship between social support and health, understandings of the meaning of social support, social networks and their inter-relationships and mechanisms remain inconclusive. Ell (1996) comments that one reason for this is that social support and health research has developed primarily through the use of descriptive epidemiological data, rather than on the basis of assumptions and hypotheses derived from robust explanatory theories. Eurelings, Diekstra and Vershuur (1995) suggest that the term 'social support' refers to a number of aspects of social relationships, but that the structure of these social relationships is often not precisely specified. It is here that our task of building a theoretical base for understanding the links between social capital and health might make a contribution to this rather woolly area of health psychology through beginning to develop a precise specification of the nature and characteristics of one particular set of social relations (those associated with the civic community that Putnam refers to) that play a role in delivering the kinds of social support that have been found to enhance health in so many epidemiological studies. In short, we speculate here that the civic community is a social network which delivers particular forms of social support to people in health-enhancing ways. Membership of such a social network puts one in the position of giving and receiving a range of forms of health-related emotional, material and instrumental support, with their associated health benefits.

Perceived inequalities

At the *organisational* level we have the concept of *relative power within organisations*. Marmot and colleagues have found that people who have power within organisations are more likely to be healthy than people who do not. Their ongoing Whitehall studies have revealed, for example, that people in the lower echelons of the organisation are four times more likely to have a heart attack than people in the upper echelons. Marmot *et al.* (1975) suggests that inequalities in health appear to be related to some underlying susceptibility factor which may be related to the enhanced feelings of control, self-esteem and self-respect which come with a high status job. Similar results have been found in research by Sapolsky (1993) on baboons in the Serengeti of Tanzania, where 'high status' baboons have been found to have better health than 'low status' baboons. Sapolsky explains these health differences in terms of *self-efficacy* – that baboons that are lower in the pecking order have less sense of control over access to fruit, choice of mate, never know when they might be beaten up by a more senior baboon and so on. The lives of these baboons is far more stressful than their higher-status peers. Not all subordinate baboons are equally unhealthy however, and this is where the concept of *social support* plays a role. Sapolsky demonstrates that baboons of low status are able to counter stress by being 'supportive' of one another (for example grooming each other leads to a lowering of the heart rate and stress response). The healthiest social subordinates are those who have friends, play with babies, groom non-sexy members of the opposite sex and so on. In short, as Sapolsky puts it: 'caring and sharing leads to health'. As we have already seen in our account of Wilkinson's (1996) work on unequal societies above, he argues that the concept of social capital provides a useful conceptual tool in the task of unravelling the mechanisms whereby levels of perceived relative deprivation have an impact on health in a positive or negative way in varyingly egalitarian societies. Wilkinson (1996) draws parallels between his own ideas and the work of Marmot and Sapolsky, among others, positing the concept of social capital as an important link in a multi-faceted picture which connects unequal social relations, perceived relative deprivation, lowered levels of social support and self-efficacy and negative health outcomes in communities.

Empowerment

At the *community level of analysis* we have the concept of empowerment. A large health promotion literature postulates empowerment as the mechanism through which successful community-based health promotion has its effects. Health-enhancing empowerment is generally agreed to derive from participation in and representation on those community and political structures which shape people's lives. Beyond this, however, community-based health promoters often have difficulty in conceptualising exactly what they mean by the 'empowerment' of local people, despite the fact that this is the key goal of most community-based health promotion programmes. Writers such as Israel *et al.* (1994), Labonte (1994) and Schultz (1995) argue for the urgent need to develop actionable definitions of empowerment as well as instruments to measure it – in the interests of developing more appropriate measures of the success or failure of health promotion programmes. They argue that in the past these have tended to focus too much on psychological, behavioural and physical outcomes of such programmes, with inadequate attention to community-based processes which facilitate or impede the attainment of desired outcomes. In specifying and measuring health promotion programme goals, attention needs to be given to both the *process* of increasing influence and control of the target groupings of interventions (through for example participation in community meetings) and the *outcome of the process* (for example actual influence over a decision that affects the community) across individual, community and societal levels. If health promotion activities need to be carried out in ways that are consistent with the concept of empowerment, such as the use of consensus decision-making, the sharing of information and power, mutual respect and support and capacity building, we still lack both qualitative and quantitative tools for planning and evaluating the success of such programmes in terms of the extent to which they contribute to the process of empowerment at the individual, community and societal levels of analysis.

Israel *et al.* (1994), Labonte (1994) and Shultz (1995) begin the task of mapping out the conceptual terrain that needs to be covered here. They argue, for example, that involvement in community and social networks leads to enhanced feelings of control among participants. Active involvement in community networks (including, for example, participation in organisations which attempt to influence public policy, or even simply taking an active role in a voluntary organisation) also results in enhanced collective problem-solving capabilities at the community level, in increased community influence and control over community resources, and through the increased likelihood that community members will believe that taking action is an effective means to influence community decisions – and as this happens, the individuals involved in such networks will experience a greater sense of personal self-efficacy. This is believed to influence health both directly and indirectly – directly insofar as people are more likely to take control of their health (for example through health-enhancing behaviours or speedy accessing of health services) if they believe that they are in control of other aspects of their lives; indirectly insofar as egalitarian societies are less stressful to their members, who are thus exposed to fewer of the health-damaging behavioural and physiological results of stress.

A sober antidote to the enthusiasm with which the idea of empowerment has been embraced by health promoters is provided in an article by Rissel (1994), entitled 'Empowerment: the holy grail of health promotion?'. He says that as yet there is inadequate evidence to support the widely held assumption within health promotion that empowerment at one level (individual, community or societal) will automatically have an impact on empowerment at another level, arguing that the individual and community levels of empowerment might represent qualitatively distinct processes. Rissel concludes that while the field of health promotion undoubtedly has much to gain from better understandings of the process of empowerment, as things currently stand the use of the concept is bedevilled by 'the lack of a clear theoretical underpinning, distortion of the concept by different users [and] measurement ambiguities' (p. 39). This debate is continuing, and the concept of social capital could make a useful contribution in the challenge of specifying which aspects of community social relations need to be promoted to enhance which levels of health-enhancing empowerment. As such it could potentially be developed into an invaluable tool for programme planning and evaluation.

Macro-social factors

At the *macro-social level of analysis* a vast amount of research points to correlations between health and people's socioeconomic status, ethnicity and gender, with higher levels of health being experienced amongst those social groupings who have the greatest access to political power (in both the personal and public spheres) and economic wealth (Blane, Brunner and Wilkinson, 1996). Factors such as age, geographical location, rural/urban residence and so on are also important macro-social influences on health (for example Macintyre, Maciver and Sooman, 1993; Macintyre and Ellaway, 1996). What relationship might exist between macro-social factors (in particular poverty) and social capital and health? This is an extremely controversial and emotionally charged topic. As mentioned above, Wilkinson (1996) suggests that the relationship between social capital and health might only exist in countries that have already undergone the epidemiological transition. On the other hand Gillies, Tolley and Wolstenholme (1996) imply that a link between health and social capital might still exist in conditions of poverty. They suggest that the damaging effects of poverty on health are mediated through the role that poverty plays in destroying social capital in deprived communities. Gillies and colleagues argue that efforts to reduce health inequalities through economic regeneration need to be accompanied by simultaneous attempts to bring about social regeneration (that is efforts to rebuild community cohesion which is undermined by poverty).

However, a range of radical thinkers such as Budlender and Dube (1998) express concern that such arguments linking health and social capital could be twisted or subverted by cost-cutting governments or policy-makers intent on justifying a retreat from welfare spending. They argue that emphasis on the role of social capital in enhancing health might divert attention away from the more urgent need to improve health through reducing income inequalities. Governments or policy-makers might use the concept of social capital as a justification for retreating from relatively costly welfare measures – in favour of the 'cheaper' option of placing the responsibility for improving health on members of deprived communities, through urging them to participate more in community life. These are clearly vitally important and complex issues that would need to be pursued in a series of careful empirical research projects in different countries and contexts. Debates such as these highlight the need for caution in allowing enthusiasm for the new and extremely promising, but still untested, concept of social capital to deflect attention from the empirically well-established link between health inequalities and poverty.

Behavioural and physiological pathways

The context of this particular review has been the field of health education, and the role that social capital might play in creating environments that maximise the likelihood that people will behave in health-promoting ways. We have also referred to the role that social capital might play in reducing anxiety and stress in the individual, thereby making him or her less vulnerable to disease. Leonardi (1997) has also pointed to the potential role of social capital as a triggering device or early warning system. Members of caring and supportive social environments are more likely to urge those who suffer ill health to seek out the appropriate health-care institutions as promptly as possible.

In the stress and social support literatures, much has been written about the way in which social stress affects health via two pathways – *behavioural* pathways (for example where stress leads to increases in smoking, drinking, teeth-grinding, coffee-drinking and other health-harming behaviours – an area of interest to health educators) and *physiological* pathways (for example through increases in blood clot formations and hence heart attacks, increases in catecholamines which lead to kidney disease and impaired immune function, increases in corticosteroids which lead to arthritis and impaired immune function). Some reference has already been made to such processes above, and more detailed reviews of this work may be found in Ogden (1996) and Stroebe and Stroebe (1995).

A model of the link between social relations and health

This chapter concludes with a diagram that seeks to locate the role social capital could play in continuing debates about the social determinants of health. The diagram also provides a schematic framework for the development of hypotheses for much-needed research into potential links between social capital and health. According to this model, social capital, that is different types of community networks and relationships (Box A), will be associated with variable levels of social support, perceived self-efficacy and perceived relative deprivation (Box B). These have a varying impact on people's physiological status (Box C) and behaviour (Box D), in ways that enhance or lower levels of health (Box E).

A1: MACRO-SOCIAL RELATIONS (e.g. gender, ethnicity, socioeconomic status, area of residence)

A2: COMMUNITY RELATIONS (levels of social capital, e.g. trust, reciprocity, civic engagement, local identity, density of local networks)

B: PSYCHO-SOCIAL MEDIATORS (e.g. self-efficacy, social support, perceived relative deprivation)

C: BEHAVIOURAL PATHWAYS (behaviours that enhance or damage health, e.g. smoking, exercise, speedy accessing of services when health problems arise)

and/or

D: PHYSIOLOGICAL PATHWAYS (impaired or optimal levels of, e.g. neuroendocrine, immunological functioning)

E: HEALTH OUTCOMES (good or bad health and wellbeing)

Pathways between social capital and health

As has already been stated, in relation to Box A, much research remains to be done regarding the interaction between social capital, and macro-social determinants of health (in particular poverty, but also gender, ethnicity, geographical location and so on).

In this review, the aim has been to locate the concept of social capital within the context of the key question currently facing health educators – if health-related behaviours are influenced by the extent to which people are located within health-enabling environments, how can such environments best be conceptualised/promoted? It is our belief that the concept of social capital provides a useful starting point in the task of investigating which types of community networks and relationships might serve to enhance people's health. Unlike the concept's 'home discipline' of political science, where much work remains to be done in explicating the mechanisms whereby social capital might have its beneficial effects (that is promote good government), an extensive literature in the social psychology and sociology of health could be drawn on in the task of explicating the mechanisms whereby social capital might have its allegedly beneficial health effects.

2. Social capital in local communities in England: the Luton pilot study

The aim of the Luton pilot study was to examine the forms taken by social capital in ward-level local communities in England; and to generate hypotheses regarding which aspects of community networks and relationships might serve to enhance levels of health. In the light of this aim this report explores people's subjective experiences of 'community' in the two socioeconomically matched (less affluent) wards of Farley (characterised by relatively low levels of health) and Sundon Park (characterised by relatively high levels of health), in the light of our hypothesis that levels of social capital will be higher in wards characterised by 'high health' than those with 'low health' (see Leonardi *et al*. for details of site selection). One of our primary goals in exploring the link between health and social capital is to examine the potential of the concept of social capital as a conceptual tool for those interested in promoting health-enabling local community contexts.

Against this background, the aims of this report are fivefold:
- to explore people's subjective experience of 'community' in each of our wards of interest;
- to do this in the light of the key dimensions of social capital as defined by Putnam (local identity, trust, reciprocity and civic engagement in local community organisations and networks);
- to investigate which factors might help or hinder the development of each of these aspects of social capital;
- to develop hypotheses regarding which types of community networks and relationships might serve as sources of health-enhancing support or health-damaging strain; and
- where necessary elaborate and rework Putnam's concept of social capital to apply to micro-communities in the UK context.

The latter goal was formulated in the light of our concern that Putnam's conceptualisation of social capital – developed in the context of research into regional government in Italy and drawing on information gleaned from local government leaders and officials as well as official statistics – might need to be amended to apply to the understandings and experiences of community life of ordinary people in ward-level local communities in England.

The role played by the concept of community in the history of health and social services in England is a controversial one. Much has been written about the shortcomings of policies relating to 'community care', for example. Many authors have commented that while these policies might have made intellectual and political sense, they were based on unrealistically optimistic assumptions about the extent to which existing community networks and resources were capable of providing adequate care and support for previously institutionalised people (for example Barnes, 1997) . By the same token it is important that health promotion policies that seek to promote health-enabling communities approach this task with a realistic understanding of the types of community networks, resources and relationships that exist in their local communities of interest, and that their conceptualisations of community resonate with the experiences and perceptions of ordinary people at the local community level.

In July and August 1997, in-depth open-ended interviews and focus groups were conducted with a small sample of people drawn from the two Luton wards of Farley and Sundon Park (a total of 48 focus group respondents and 37 in-depth interview respondents). The size and nature of our sample limit our ability to draw definitive conclusions about our communities of interest. However, the richness and depth of the material we have collected allow us to begin to isolate the types of local issues, networks and relationships that might exist as a resource for health promoters.

The empirical findings of this study are presented in Chapters 3 to 7. Chapter 3 reports on the focus group study which aimed to provide a thumbnail sketch of community life in the two wards, and to provide orienting accounts of people's perceptions of local identity, trust, reciprocal help and support, and civic engagement – which constitute Putnam's criteria for social capital.

Chapter 4 examines local people's perceptions of community in the light of the rhetorical device of past–present comparisons – which interview participants frequently used in giving an account of contemporary community life. Although past–present comparisons usually romanticise the past, and are very often historically inaccurate, for our purposes they provided a rich source of information about people's subjective perceptions of those aspects of community life which served as sources of strain or sources of support. Furthermore, people's accounts of the 'past' were consistent with Putnam's conceptualisation of social capital in terms of community cohesion characterised by trust, reciprocity and local identity. Our interviews provided detailed insights into the way in which the working and living conditions of late twentieth-century England limited the development of these community virtues – highlighting the need for a reworking of Putnam's account of what constitutes a 'civic community' if it is to serve as a useful conceptual tool for investigating those potentially health-enhancing dimensions of local community life.

While the four dimensions of social capital: trust, local identity, reciprocity and civic engagement are closely inter-linked, Chapter 4 places greater emphasis on trust, reciprocity and local identity, as opposed to Chapters 5, 6 and 7, which emphasise civic engagement in a variety of community networks – that according to Putnam constituted the source of the high levels of trust, reciprocity and local identity constituting social capital. Chapter 5 focuses on informal face-to-face networks of relatives and friends, Chapter 6 on voluntary associations related to leisure, hobbies and personal development and Chapter 7 on formal and informal community activist groups and initiatives.

Against this background, Chapter 8 concludes by highlighting differences in social capital in our high-health and low-health communities. In the light of divergences between people's accounts of contemporary community life in England and Putnam's definition of what constitutes a civic community, the report concludes by highlighting a number of ways in which Putnam's concept needs to be modified to apply to conditions in England, and by highlighting which dimensions of social capital might be the most promising resources for health promotional work in local community contexts.

3. Setting the context: perceptions of social capital in Farley and Sundon Park

Putnam (1993a) characterises social capital as the community cohesion which results from high levels of local identity, trust, reciprocal help and support, and civic engagement. This chapter reports on a focus group study which explored people's subjective experiences of local community relationships in the wards of Farley (low health) and Sundon Park (high health) in Luton. These exploratory groups highlight differences in the forms of social capital in the two wards. In summary, robust relationships of *reciprocal help and support* between close friends and neighbours existed in both communities. In Farley (the low-health district) there appeared to be higher levels of *local identity*, and more *local facilities* (such as a council-provided community centre) as well as more extensive street-based youth peer networks. Farley people's lives tended to centre more in the local community than their Sundon Park counterparts. Sundon Park (high health) appeared to exhibit higher levels of *trust* amongst its community members, as well as higher levels of *confidence in the political power of ordinary citizens*.

The focus groups provide a starting point – which will be built on in our analysis of the in-depth interviews – for a number of important ways in which Putnam's notion of social capital needs to be reworked, two of which are mentioned here. Firstly we will argue that certain dimensions of social capital might be more relevant to health than others. In terms of its potential as a conceptual tool for pinpointing those aspects of community that enable and support healthy behaviours and which serve as a buffer against health-damaging stress and strain, Putnam's definition might need to be disaggregated. In particular we will argue that in relation to health, greater attention needs to be paid to the phenomena of trust and perceived citizen power/civic engagement, with less emphasis on local place-based community identities.

This leads to our second related argument, which starts from our finding that the community identities of informants from Sundon Park (our high-health ward) were both narrower and wider than their Farley counterparts. Farley residents had strong local place-based identities. By contrast, while they were at home, the focus of Sundon Park people's lives often lay within the four walls of home, rather than in the streets and public spaces. However, more importantly, away from home, Sundon Park people's social networks extended beyond the boundaries of the geographical ward to include a range of non-local networks. In later chapters we will argue that narrow place-based identities and networks (of the Farley type) might be less beneficial than networks and identities that are more widely dispersed.

Focus group methodology

Eight focus groups were conducted, four in the ward of Farley and four in the ward of Sundon Park. These groups were held in the Farley Community Centre and in a private home in Sundon Park respectively.* The groups were recruited by a market research company, who selected the sample according to the categories of gender, age and ward of residence. Each mixed-gender group consisted of six to eight members, half male and half female, falling into four age ranges (15–18, 19–34, 35–55 and 55+). Each group lasted two hours, and time was equally divided among the following six topics:

1. What are the main life challenges facing people of your age group in Farley/Sundon Park? (This information provided contextual background for the other five topics.)
2. To what extent is there a sense of local identity or belongingness amongst Farley/Sundon Park residents?
3. To what extent can and do residents of Farley/Sundon Park trust one another?
4. To what extent can residents of Farley/Sundon Park rely on one another for help and support?
5. What are people's attitudes to local politics and to the potential power of ordinary citizens to shape community affairs?
6. What are the informal and formal group memberships available to people of your age group?

There is much debate regarding the reliability and validity of focus group studies: the extent to which the information they generate should be regarded as preliminary

---

*The community centre serving the Sundon Park ward was located in what was widely viewed as a less desirable part of the ward, and informants were reluctant to go there at night when the groups were held.

hypothesis-generating material or substantive research data; and whether their findings have weight beyond that of providing corroborating evidence in multi-method research designs (Lunt and Livingstone, 1996). The claims we make on the basis of our focus group data are modest, and it should be remembered that the current study is an exploratory one. At most we seek to generate hypotheses regarding the forms that social capital might take in high- and low-health communities, rather than providing an in-depth study of two particular Luton wards. (For this reason it is strongly emphasised that where, for example, we cite views that are critical of local services or politicians, these are the views of a small sample of people, gathered in pursuit of research goals relating to the academic goal of conceptual exploration and development. We do not aim to provide an accurate portrait of community life in particular wards.) Furthermore this focus group information is part of a multi-method research programme, and should be located within the context of the in-depth interview study in the following section, as well as continuing work such as the survey study by Leonardi *et al.* (in preparation) of social capital in our wards of interest.

This chapter of the report has three sections. The first section presents a detailed description of the findings of the Farley (low-health) focus groups and the second section describes the issues that emerged in the Sundon Park (high-health) focus groups. This descriptive material is included as the contextual backdrop for material presented in later chapters of this report. *Readers might choose to omit the descriptive detail and focus on the summaries of each section (Farley summary, pp. 45–47; Sundon Park summary, pp. 60–61) and the concluding section of this chapter (pp. 62–67).* The final section of this chapter highlights differences in the quality of relationships in the two wards, in the light of Putnam's (1993a) categories of local identity, trust, reciprocal help and support, and attitudes to local government.

Farley focus groups

1. Farley: life challenges

The major stress facing the **15–18 year age group** was boredom, linked to the lack of facilities and opportunities for recreation and leisure. Because of this, young people ended up 'hanging about' near shops, in parks or on street corners, in groups ranging from 5 or 10 to 40 or 50 – smoking, playing football or '*getting into trouble*' of various sorts (including '*fighting, occasionally thieving, breaking windows and annoying people in general*'). As a result of this, they were aware that they had a negative image in the community which contributed to a feeling of resentment, particularly on the frequent occasions where they believed that their misdemeanours were exaggerated or where they were scapegoated for problems or offences which they had not committed. Adults were frequently described as unjustifiably negative ('*moany*') and punitive towards them. This negative image also led to a collective sense of rejection by the community at large. This contributed to a sense of low self-esteem.

There was a tension in young people's accounts of their day-to-day lives in the Farley community. On the one hand they spoke of peer pressures to smoke, drink, act in a '*hard*' (tough) way, and generally test the limits of parents, teachers, the police and other community adults – and they also communicated a keen sense of the pleasure and excitement that they derived from these activities. On the other hand they felt that they might have benefited from more non-punitive discipline, guidance, tolerance and caring from the adults in their lives – and in some sense felt that the community had let them down in this respect. Thus for example older members of the 15–18 group spoke regretfully of how having '*messed about*' at school, they were struggling in their attempts to enter the job market, both because they had poor grades and bad reputations, but also because they now in retrospect believed that discipline at an early age prepared young people for the demands of the job market. ('*You need to have had discipline to keep a job . . . if you are used to being told what to do and accepting it . . . but we don't get this discipline when we are growing up.*') They spoke vaguely of their future hopes – to make money, have a good job, car, house, spouse and family, but were not all terribly optimistic that these goals were within their reach. ('*Young people act badly out of school, mess about with crime and stuff, give cheek in school to the teachers . . . then they get bad results in their exams, no job, on the dole, then really crap jobs.*')

Concerns of the **19- to 34-year-old group** included the difficulties of finding work, in particular for mothers who lacked experience and who might be considered too old to start learning particular jobs, and who were burdened with the additional problem of finding affordable child care to enable them to work. Both male and female informants in this group referred to the poor pay of the jobs that were available to them, often offering little more than the unemployment benefit would give them. People referred to constant worries about bills and generally making ends meet, as well as the fact that they seldom had any money left over for entertainment or leisure.

The two main preoccupations of the **35- to 55-year-old group** were stresses relating to teenage children, and to financial problems. With regard to children, people said they faced the pressures of children who had reached the age where they wanted to go out, but lacked suitable places to go to. They worried about their children becoming part of '*bad crowds*' that hung about in public spaces. The community centre was inadequate to meet the social needs of the large number of teenagers in the area, besides which community centre activities cost money, and were often beyond the reach of parents, especially those on income support. Money and the rising cost of living was their second concern, with people feeling that there were no safety nets into which they could fall were serious financial crises to arise.

Informants in the **55+ age group** spoke of the stresses of the rising cost of living, fears that they lacked adequate funds for health care or nursing if they became frail, the stress of caring for sick spouses, the isolation of those who lived alone. In particular they referred to the stresses of the endless forms they had to fill in for accessing benefits, organising burials and so on – and of the inefficiency of the agencies in charge of benefit allocation. Another major stress was the long waits that often resulted between GP referrals and appointments with specialists. ('*Once you reach a* *certain age you're regarded as rubbish, as past your sell-by date by the medics.*') Changes in the country's welfare system had left many older people feeling vulnerable and unprepared. ('*Everyone's dream is to have a comfortable retirement, to leave something for the children, to have a decent funeral. Sometimes we fear that all our carefully worked out plans are being hijacked.*')

2. Farley: local identity

There was a strong sense of identity amongst youth peer groups in Farley, with these groups being strongly defined in geographical terms. The **15- to 18-year-olds** spoke of a recent incident where a group from another suburb had arrived in cars with baseball bats to attack the local youths, and they described the strong sense of local solidarity which was demonstrated in this incident ('*we were all there for each other, we all knew each other, and that we would all stick up for one another . . . the more fights there are, the more we stick up for each other*'). While membership of informal youth peer groups was seen as a source of positive social identity in the micro-local context, young people worried that they had an unjustifiably bad reputation in the Luton community as a whole ('*people outside Farley see us as thieves, trouble-makers and arsonists*') and they felt that this image had a negative effect on their chances of getting jobs in Luton.

The **19- to 34-year-olds** and **35- to 55-year-olds** also expressed a strong sense of positive local belongingness in Farley, describing it as one of the '*most wanted*' areas in Luton. They described its location as particularly favourable – located close not only to the city centre but also to the countryside. They appreciated the fact that it was a small area, with well-built houses, and that many council tenants had exercised their 'right to buy', resulting in a sense of permanence and commitment to the area.

People who had grown up there valued sharing a common history with many people such as old school friends. People who moved away from Farley often moved back because they missed their Farley social networks. Even those informants who were relative newcomers to the ward reported that it had a 'nice atmosphere' with people chatting in the shops and generally being favourably disposed towards one another. Despite some disadvantages, such as noisy children, intimidating gangs of teenagers and young men racing their cars around the district, people regarded Farley as attractive and congenial. People often had conversations with one another in the street, and pedestrians would often compliment skilful gardeners as they walked down the street.

People said that 'community spirit' was particularly strong among those neighbours that lived in closes, where people could watch one another come and go, and thus look out for one another's safety and wellbeing – although this surveillance could sometimes spill over into nosiness or even unpleasantness (for example neighbours who might report a woman for claiming single parent's benefit after noticing that she had a live-in partner).

Unlike the other age groups, the **55+ age group** said that while Farley had once been considered one of the best wards in Luton, because of rising crime and anti-social groups of teenagers it was fast becoming one of the worst. They did not see the Farley community as one that was particularly supportive of old people, and compared to the past, there was not much community spirit or neighbourliness in the ward, and people had far less informal contact with others in the neighbourhood. One of the reasons they cited for the perceived decline in the general sense of local belongingness was the changing community composition. Too many problem families were being moved into the ward from other areas. Over the years increasingly fewer people lived in extended or even nuclear families, with many households consisting only of mothers and children, mothers who were often too burdened with responsibilities to participate in community life. An increasingly diverse ethnic mix was also changing the fabric of the Farley community. Reference was made to the growing number of Asian families. While they tended to be quiet and considerate neighbours, they would *'stick to themselves'* socially rather than integrating with non-Asian neighbours. All these factors contributed to their sense that the community was more fragmented than it had been in the past.

3. Farley: trust

Focus group respondents understood the notion of trust to refer to a situation where people could assume that others would act in their best interests, in particular through: (i) showing a tolerant and positive attitude towards them; (ii) acting in a way that was respectful of their physical safety and the safety of their property (with the latter case not only referring to issues such as theft or damage, but also with regard to returning items or money that had been borrowed); and (iii) respecting their privacy through taking care not to repeat information they had confided in you, as well as refraining from damaging their good reputation through gossip.

The **15–18 year age group** spoke of generalised positive attitudes amongst members of teenage peer groups (*'young people trust the young, they all stick together'*), but said that as a general principle one should not trust people with confidential information or property until one knew them very well. Several spoke of peers who had stolen small items (for example headphones, cassette tapes) or small sums of money when visiting their houses. They spoke of low levels of inter-generational trust, particularly between the youth and elderly people – saying that neither group showed adequate respect or tolerance of the other. At different stages of the discussion blame for this situation was assigned to each of the two groups. Sometimes the youth spoke more sympathetically of the old people's life in the community. (*'I would say that Farley is not a pleasant place for older people. No one gives them respect. If we are playing football and making a noise, they start telling us to get lost and we just swear back at them.'*) At other times they portrayed old people as unjustifiably intolerant and vindictive. (*'The old people are really really moany in our area and shout at us for no reason and things like that'*; and *'Older people, they don't respect us. We can't do nothing right in their eyes. We go to one place and they tell us to go away. We go to another place and other old people moan about us. One person last week even phoned the police on us and took pictures of us hanging about in the park – yet we weren't doing nothing wrong at all.'*) At other times they simply appeared bewildered at the fear they sometimes inspired in elderly fellow residents. (*'A big group of us were once hanging about outside the Co-op and one old woman wouldn't come out of the shop until we had gone . . . she was scared we were all going to jump her . . . they always think we are going to hurt them – why do they think this? We would help them if anyone was trying to mug them.'*)

Informants in the **19- to 34-year-old group** said that while they would trust people that they knew personally, one had to be wary of those one did not know. When asked why, they answered (partly sardonically) that one could never know these days if someone was a *'nutter, a burglar or a drug addict'*. More seriously they commented that one had to guard against *'people trying to take advantage of you'*, or people who might gossip about one's private affairs, borrow money and not repay it or harm your children in some way. A number of people referred to experiences where they had not been paid for work they had done in various casual jobs. In terms of borrowing and lending among neighbours, they said that while they would gladly lend a neighbour some eggs or sugar in an emergency, it was as well never to lend more than one could afford to lose on the assumption that it might not be returned.

The aspect of trust that informants in the **35- to 55-year-old group** said was most relevant to community life was the issue of being able to confide in others about one's private lives, triumphs and troubles. People were very wary of becoming the victims of gossip. Trust of other community members built up over a long period of time – either through getting to know them personally, or through the recommendations of trusted friends – but on the whole people felt that one should err on the side of caution in this regard. (*'It's probably better to keep people at a distance – help each other out, but don't confide too much.'*) Older people were generally considered more trustworthy than younger people as a rule. This was because they tended to be *'less competitive, more settled and more at peace with themselves'*.

Both the **19–34** and the **35- to 55-year-old groups** referred to stresses associated with large groups of teenagers hanging about in public places which made many people feel nervous to walk around at night. (*'You have to be tough and assertive to survive here or the teenagers and children would make your life hell.'*) They regretted the lack of community facilities to occupy these young people. Tensions also occasionally arose around ethnic issues. People cited examples where black or Asian people had been harassed, or where Scottish or Irish people had been mocked in pubs. However on the whole different ethnic groups seemed to live side by side fairly amicably.

The **55+ age group** said that older Farley people felt vulnerable to crime, as well as feeling intimidated by groups of teenagers. They felt particularly unsafe walking about at night, and even during the day felt wary if they heard footsteps behind them. They referred to living in constant fear of intruders, with elderly flat dwellers feeling reluctant to leave their flats at night – which involved having to negotiate staircases crowded with smoking and drinking teenagers. (*'In Farley these days, people live in fear. We daren't open our doors.'*) They felt that the presence of the police was inadequate for the needs of the community – and said that fear of crime took its toll on the health of old people in the ward. In particular they referred to recent incidents where pensioners had been warned about young people hanging about outside the post office and stealing people's pensions.

Comparing contemporary Farley to 'the old days', they regretted the general fear of strangers in the community, which made people reluctant to communicate with those they did not know. Older people said that while they trusted one another, they did not trust the younger age groups. They spoke of the old days where Farley had been considered a particularly desirable area of residence – one where one could leave keys with neighbours or under the mat for repair men, where one could give one's rent money to a neighbour to pay for you, and where if one knew one member of a family, one could automatically rely on and trust every other family member – contrasting this with modern life where people were more wary of one another.

4. Farley: reciprocal help and support

When asked about levels of reciprocal help and support in the community, people referred to practical help with everyday life demands, emotional support in times of stress and crisis as well as assistance in emergencies. With regard to practical issues, the **15–18 age group** said that while that they would occasionally get involved with helping neighbours with baby-sitting or car maintenance, on the whole it was their parents who interacted with neighbours – given that young people spent so little time at home. With regard to emotional or family stresses, girls said that they might consider discussing these among one or two close friends, but that one had to be wary of gossip. Boys would not discuss personal problems among themselves, but might occasionally consider confiding in a girl.

The **19- to 34-year-old group** believed that on the whole Farley residents could be relied on to look out for one another or help each other if there was a crisis. They spoke of a recent incident where a pub had been attacked by *'a group of outsiders'*, and reported approvingly that Farley residents had come out in large numbers, some armed with baseball bats, to show solidarity. In non-crisis situations people said that they would be less likely to turn to or rely on local people for support, turning first to family and close friends who did not necessarily live in their immediate neighbourhood. The only exception here was a single mother, who said that she was part of an extremely supportive network of single mothers in her street. She believed that single parents often helped each other out more than other residents – partly because they had so much in common in terms of life demands, and secondly because they tended to spend more time together in the absence of other live-in adults to communicate with. People felt that they had less contact with neighbours than would have been the case 'in the old days'. They said that this was partly due to concerns about crime, which made people more wary about letting small children play in the street – whereas in the old days, parents of such small children would have invariably got to know one another through their children's contact.

Informants in the **33- to 55-year-old group** spoke of a relaxed neighbourly atmosphere in Farley, where people felt free to borrow one another's tools and to talk to one another over the fence. With regard to offering one another more tangible help and support, people in this age group also said that they turned first to family and friends rather than to local people, although they felt confident that neighbours would come to their aid in the case of a major catastrophe such as a fire or an accident.

Older (55+) people said they often felt reluctant to ask one another for help. When asked for help people were often suspicious about the asker's motives or worried that if they offered help once they would end up with burdensome responsibilities. (*'Once there was a natural sympathy towards the old and the handicapped. Now people are more individualistic. They worry that if they show sympathy to* *someone they will get lumbered with their problems.'*) They felt they did not get the support or respect they deserved from young people. Inter-generational relations were very different to *'the old days'*. They wistfully remembered the days when older people were greeted as 'Mr' and 'Mrs', where younger people would help them carry heavy bags, and where children would give up their seats on the bus if they saw an old person struggling to stand. (*'I'm sure the young aren't bad people – they are just scatter-brained and thoughtless. Sometimes I wish we could cripple all of them – just for one day each – and see if that would help them understand our predicament better . . . they all seem tuned in to the yuppie idea that we should all look after ourselves.'*) Lack of communication was cited as the main reason for declining community spirit. (*'Perhaps if more young people and old people chatted at bus stops they would understand our life demands and be more prepared to help.'*) Their own attempts to help young people were frequently rebuffed. (*'Just this morning I went from the back of the bus to help a woman struggling with a child and pram and she was quite nasty to me.'* or *'I offered a pregnant woman my seat on the bus and she told me rudely that I looked as if I needed it more than she did.'*)

Despite this, they said that many of them had received good help from neighbours – particularly in health-related emergencies. In non-emergency situations, they got more help from people of their own age group than from younger people. (*'We are too proud to ask them, but anyway, young people are too busy with their own lives. They don't want to know about our difficulties.'*) They made a sharp distinction between the *'wonderful support'* neighbours would extend in emergencies, and the lack of any sense of community in smaller ways (for example greeting one another, politeness to strangers, non-intimidating children and so on). Furthermore they said that even the wonderful support in emergencies was 'minimalist help' compared to the old days. (*'People cover until the ambulance comes, but there's nothing ongoing as there used to be – people would worry about your washing, shopping, collecting children from school. These days they let the authorities turn up and take over – then they heave a sigh of relief, and say "Thank God I'm out of that now." In the old days they would have thought about the children – these days the police will phone social services and get them to pick the children up from school.'*)

5. Farley: attitudes to local government

Despite the fact that community development workers emphasised the dedication and commitment of many Farley local councillors (see p. 46), informants' attitudes to local government were mixed. The **15- to 18-year-old group** had no interest in or knowledge about formal local politics. However they did refer to involvement in local community initiatives. They had frequently been involved in signing local community petitions (*'loads and loads of petitions'*), particularly for a new swimming pool, and had participated in fetes and sponsored walks aimed at raising money for community facilities. In their experience such participation had been fruitless. (*'They keep telling us there is no money to do things for us, but we have raised money before and we haven't seen nothing come of it.'* and *'Interviewer: Who should take responsibility for trying to improve community facilities? Group: We should take part in this, but like every time we do do it, we don't get nothing out of it, so nobody bothers any more.'*) They said they would be willing to participate in any community-improving events that were put forward. (*'If they gave us stuff to do, if they told us some things to do, we could* *do them. But no one wants to do it, to be involved with us.'*)

They referred approvingly to *'some good adults'* amongst community leaders – both paid workers and volunteers at the community centre, but were despondent about others who were less understanding and tolerant. For example, they spoke of their anger at the unjustness of accusations made about their age group at a community centre meeting to discuss vandalism of facilities. (*'At this meeting they told us they couldn't do anything for us because we would just break it . . . most of us just walked out because they were blaming everything on us – even the things that are done by the younger kids.'*) While they expressed admiration and respect for some of the police, they felt others were not sympathetic to the constraints facing young people in the area. (*'We have nowhere to go, nothing to do. We play football in the street and they come and take the ball away and we have to go to the station to collect it. and I go, "Well, there's nowhere for us to play." He goes, "Well, I used to walk fifteen miles every day to play football." As if I'm going to walk fifteen miles to play football! Just a little twenty-minute game.'*)

The **19- to 34-year-olds** expressed unanimous discontent with the local council. For example, they felt that council maintenance work was contracted out to *'cowboy contractors'*, who were often negligent or dishonest. They felt that the council also failed the community in terms of providing adequate child-care facilities, and adequate facilities for older children. In particular there were strong negative feelings about the council's refusal to take heed of the community's long fight to have a swimming pool in the area. (*'I signed my first petition for a swimming pool when I was 10, and we are still waiting 21 years later.'*) Furthermore they resented the fact that the council sometimes gave building contracts to companies outside of Luton, rather than ensuring that local people were employed on local projects. People were sceptical about the value of voting. (*'There is no point in voting – it's a complete waste of time. They all tell lies and are as bad as each other.'*) Apart from their perception of politicians as dishonest, they felt they were out of touch with the needs of the ordinary people in their wards, and failed to take adequate time or trouble to find out what their views were.

People in this group expressed unanimous dissatisfaction with the police. They said that the police were often slow to turn up when called out, and often did not seem interested in the community they served. They said that this increased people's sense of vulnerability to crime. All the Farley focus groups expressed resentment about a recent newspaper report about a 'riot' in the ward, where people believed that the police had given the journalist inaccurate information stating that the trouble was caused by conflicting youth gangs in Farley – when in fact they believed it had been started by an outside gang, with Farley youth acting purely in self-defence. They said that such inaccurate information had the potential to give the ward an unjustifiably bad name. One of the group members had participated in a community meeting organised by the tenants' and residents' association to discuss this conflict. However she felt that the meeting had been unfocused and had failed to yield any possible results. (*'It just makes me think "what's the point", i.e. of making an effort to attend such meetings.'*)

Informants in the **35–55 age group** were divided in their assessment of the effectiveness of local politics, with some saying that it offered people an opportunity to contribute to community affairs, and others saying that they resented politicians that invaded their privacy by coming to their doors and making false promises in order to get elected. In general the consensus was that politicians probably could not be trusted, and that when all was said and done they did not listen to the voices of ordinary people. On the whole they felt that Farley people tended to be apathetic about community affairs. ('*People tend to sit back and say "let someone else do it".*')

People in the **55+ age group** also felt that the council was not guided by local people's views. Attempts to raises issues of council shortcomings at local surgeries were always shrugged off with the excuse that there was no money. They too felt the council was particularly deficient in its task of maintaining property. Contractors were slapdash. Street cleaning was shoddy, the dog-fouling act was inadequately enforced, and policing was inadequate.

6. Farley: significant formal and informal group memberships

For the **15- to 18-year-olds** the only group that appeared to have any importance or influence was that of the informal peer group – with groups ranging from 5 to 40 members, and group membership being determined by area of residence rather than by other factors such as school (young people in Farley attended a number of different schools). They cited the main activities of such groupings as 'hanging about' and smoking, and on Friday nights drinking. They spoke of strong peer pressures to drink and smoke (*'people in my group drink and smoke to act big in front of one another'*), despite being aware of the health risks (*'you know it might affect your future, but not yet it won't'*). While they referred to voluntary groupings that they might have joined such as the Scouts, Guides, church and aerobics classes these were generally described as '*boring*' or '*pointless*'. Participation in aerobics classes would open one to ridicule. (*'Everyone would take the mick if they saw me prancing about in a leotard.'*)

Some reference was made to the Rotherham youth club which met on Tuesday evenings – and provided activities such as cards, pool, television and football, but these were generally rejected as '*boring*'. More positive references were made to the Farley Community Centre which sometimes arranged activities such as outings (these appeared to be very highly regarded), and also for example hired out a room with a pool table to a maximum of six people for 80p an evening, however it seems that the centre was dominated by one particularly '*hard*' group of young people, who were generally avoided by other groups.

Those in the **19- to 34-year-old group** spoke of a number of different groupings in the wards, including the church (*'boring, a load of rubbish'*), the pub (*'for some, the only place they know'*), aerobics classes and the youth club (*'crap'*). On the whole people in their age group did not participate much in such activities. Because two of the members of the group had been involved in setting up and running the local 'community caff', there was much discussion of this as a case study of a community-motivated enterprise. This initiative had been instigated by both the council and a small grouping of local residents. The council had provided much of the funding, and paid the rent, and the caff was staffed by a group of unpaid volunteers. However this group of volunteers was small and over-extended, and the caff had recently had to drastically reduce its opening hours in the absence of further volunteers. People said there was little motivation in the community to volunteer – most people prioritised their own interests (*'people are concerned with their own interests rather than the community – and they don't see how volunteering is going to benefit them in the long run'*); they were lazy (*'people would rather sit at home and watch the telly than work for nothing'*) or they felt that the general political context did not encourage them to participate (*'some people think: the council and the government don't help me – so why should I put an effort into helping them improve the community'*). Others were just inherently passive (*'even those who appreciate the help that volunteers provide the community are not prepared to contribute themselves'*). And even those who might have been motivated lacked the time to put into such activities, particularly if they were working or had small children.

Caff volunteers were looked upon with scepticism or contempt by many, who could not see the point of voluntary work (*'people are sceptical of why we do it – they feel that in some way we are going to benefit personally from this work, so are doing it for our own sakes rather than that of the community'*; *'people call us mugs for working for no money'*; *'it's considered naff to volunteer'*).

One of the members of the group, an unemployed man of 21, had strong views about the need for a better youth club in the community, but said that a range of obstacles stood in the way of such an activity being initiated by an ordinary person like himself. Firstly he pointed to lack of finance and to his lack of organisational skills. He doubted if the council would back a community group initiated by someone like him. He dwelt heavily on the fact that he had no GCSEs, and that someone with so little education was unlikely to be taken seriously. (*'I would need to go to college – to work with young people you need to have certificates.'*) He also expressed a general lack of confidence in several ways. (*'No one knows me – why should anyone trust me?'*; *'I've got nothing to show that I could actually do it and make a success of it. I can't go up to somebody and say "believe in me because it will happen", because at the end of the day it might well backfire and then it won't happen.'*) While one group member disagreed with him, saying that if he were to start off as a volunteer in an existing group, he might later move on to initiating his own group, others agreed with him that it was extremely difficult for an ordinary person to initiate successful community activities. In short this discussion pointed to a general lack of confidence in the power of ordinary young people to initiate or participate in successful community-building activities.

Informants in the **19–34 age group** spoke favourably of the local Neighbourhood Watch, but said that sometimes it gave more trouble-making residents the opportunity to cause unnecessary trouble (for example reporting neighbours whose car licence discs had expired). There had been some attempt to set up a credit union, but this had been unsuccessful. They referred to groupings such as the youth club, Irish dancing, the St Margaret's Club, the community centre and the local pub, where men in particular were often very preoccupied with pool competitions. They did not know much about the community caff other than the fact that many younger mothers were not drawn to it because it had no space for children to play in. They emphasised the need for more activities for children as a community-building exercise. (*'When children are happy and off the streets, we all benefit.'*) They felt that more sporting activities might be a good way of keeping young people busy, but emphasised that most parents would find it difficult to pay for these, particularly if they had more than one child.

Informal groups referred to by the **55+ age group** consisted of the pub, St Margaret's Church Club, the Evergreen club, bingo at the community centre. Older people spoke dismissively of the Farley Tenants' Association. They felt that it was an elitist organisation, dominated by a small group of relatively well-off people who reflected neither the composition nor the interests of the majority of Farley citizens. (*'Some of us are reluctant to join because we are made to feel that we are not good enough.'*) The activities that this grouping arranged were generally too expensive for most older people to participate in. They said that there was a great need for affordable outings for elderly people to 'go to new places'. They liked the community caff. They felt that more should be done for single old people in the community, and regretted the fact that the church and priests played far less of a role in this regard than they used to.

Summary: subjective perceptions of social capital in Farley

There was a strong positive sense of *local identity and belongingness* amongst the 15- to 55-year-olds in Farley. It was considered a particularly favourable geographical location (close to the city centre and the countryside), and a place where people chose to spend their whole lives, or to return to after they had left. Many residents shared a long history of co-residence and familiarity, which formed the backdrop for a pleasant and congenial atmosphere in public places. The 55+ age group expressed the least favourable sense of local identity, saying that over the years Farley had become less safe and less cohesive, and that the culture of politeness and caring that had typified the community in earlier days had given way to a far more aggressive and individualistic atmosphere.

People were more qualified in their views about levels of *trust* in Farley. While they generally said that one could trust people that one knew, and people of one's own age group, they would always be very cautious of those they did not know well. Trust between people of different age groups was in particularly short supply. In particular, people referred to the 10–18 age group as a negative force in the community – often hostile, aggressive and anti-social (although all emphasised that the 'youth problem' was partly due to the lack of facilities for young people and the unwillingness or fear of parents and other adults to give young people the support and discipline they needed). In their turn, the 15–18s said that the negative image of the under-18s was exaggerated, and that they had become scapegoats for too many community ills.

With regard to *giving and receiving help and support*, people were confident that in emergencies and crises, others would come to their aid, but that in non-crisis situations people tended to devote their (often limited) energies and resources to their own immediate families and/or selves. Views were patchy however. It seemed that many people did have supportive relationships with particular friends and neighbours, but that these relationships were quite specific and did not generalise beyond particular neighbours and beyond particular contexts.

People's *perceptions of local government* and of potential *grassroots citizen-power* were unambiguously negative. Politicians were described as untrustworthy, not particularly interested in the views of their constituents, with many of them out of touch with the needs and wishes of ordinary people. The local council was seen as inefficient (for example poor property maintenance, street-cleaning) and having failed to deliver on crucial community needs – in particular needs for child-care facilities and recreational facilities for young people. Informants regretted that attempts to complain to politicians and counsellors about their performance were often brushed aside with the excuse that there was no money for community improvements. Political involvement by ordinary people was repeatedly described as 'pointless' – thus for example the local tenants' and residents' association was seen as toothless and ineffectual, large numbers of local petitions had failed to bear fruit over the years, and young people referred to numerous fetes, sponsored walks and so on which had been organised to raise money for community facilities which had never materialised. In short, the focus groups painted a picture of a group of people who did not regard local political structures as representative of their views or capable of meeting their needs. Furthermore, there was little faith in the power of ordinary citizens to have any impact on local politics or community affairs.

(Here it must be emphasised that in informal discussions of our focus group findings, community development workers expressed the view that over the years Farley had been fortunate to have some particularly dedicated and hard-working local representatives, who had served the community with great energy and commitment. However, the focus groups suggest that the efforts of such representatives might have had less than their optimal effects in creating social capital in Farley, see p. 41)

With regard to *formal and informal voluntary groupings*, there were a range of formal activities and groups (for example youth groups, aerobics classes, the local pub and so on), but people were unenthusiastic about these. There seemed to be minority cliques, particularly among the 15–18 and the 55+ age groups, which functioned to exclude many residents from participating in the tenants' association and certain community centre activities. People felt that there was a particularly pressing need for more organising around the needs and interests of both the youth and the elderly, but that in the absence of sustained commitment and motivation by the council and confidence, commitment and motivation on the part of ordinary citizens, such organisation was unlikely to happen.

(Here again, in contrast to focus group informants, community development workers said that council-linked agencies have put effort and resources into establishing community services and initiatives in Farley. In Chapter 7 we suggest that it might be the case that while great initial effort is put into setting these up, more attention needs to be paid to optimising access and sustainability, and that such projects need to be conceptualised in a more long-term, phased manner – ranging from initial set-up to long-term sustainability.)

In short, despite a mostly positive sense of local identity in Farley, levels of trust and reciprocity tended to be patchy and non-generalised, and there was little faith in local government and little confidence in the ability or motivation of ordinary people to participate in local community improvement. People tended to be unenthusiastic about local social organisations and activities, and those activities that did exist were patchily used, often by small minorities.

Sundon Park focus groups

1. Life challenges

In the Sundon Park **15- to 18-year-old group**, stresses revolved around passing examinations, and worrying about finding jobs. Such stresses were often intensified for those who had problems at home, such as divorcing. They emphasised how their lives differed from those of their parents as teenagers. Parents were less strict these days, and had reason to be far more concerned about their teenage children's safety with higher crime levels, and greater dangers facing young people who came home late. They complained about the lack of facilities in the ward, saying there was little to do beyond *'sitting at home and getting bored'*, playing football in the streets, and going to friends' houses. Sports facilities at the local school were not open to the public, and there was no community centre. They dissociated themselves from the community centre at Marsh Farm on the edge of the Sundon Park ward, saying that this was not regarded as part of Sundon Park, and that their parents discouraged them from going there because of the area's bad reputation for crime, drugs and rioting.

People in the **19- to 34-year-age group**, often with young children, cited stresses about money and employment (finding jobs, or fears about redundancy) as their major life concerns. In addition they worried about the demands that their young children were going to have to face in the future – disadvantaged by pressures to perform at under-resourced schools in an increasingly competitive world, with fewer opportunities for young people.

The **35- to 55-year-olds** spoke of worries about bills and mortgages (*'financial stress is there all the time, it never goes away'*). Adequately paid jobs were in short supply, and wages had often not kept up with inflation. Part-time contract work was becoming increasingly common with the associated loss of rights and holiday money. Trade unions were less powerful. (*'Lots of people here are trying to pay mortgages and bring up families on £2.50 or £3 an hour.'*) They also spoke of worries that their children might get into bad company, or start taking drugs.

Issues facing younger members of the **55+ age group** involved decisions about when to give up work and how best to organise one's finances in anticipation of retirement. For the others, health was their overriding concern. People had had variable experiences with the health services, some being satisfied and others citing problems they had had with GPs and hospitals.

2. Sundon Park: local identity

People in the **15- to 18-year-old group** were unanimous that there was no sense of local identity as a Sundon Park resident. (*'The fact that I live in Sundon Park means nothing to me.'*) Several went further and said that they would move away from the area if they had the chance, saying that they would prefer to bring up their children in a place where there was more for them to do, and which had a *'better reputation'*. Here they referred to the fact that while Sundon Park itself was a relatively quiet area, it was located between the areas of Hockwell Ring and Marsh Farm, both of which had been in the news for *'rioting and causing trouble'*.

Entertainment-wise, they said the area was geographically far from the city centre and very quiet and dull for young people. (*'In Sundon Park we are kind of away, tucked out of town like . . . parents move up here because they want somewhere quiet to live for when they are older and where they are not going to get trouble, it's quiet and boring here.'*) However they did not think Sundon Park was any worse than other parts of Luton, which in general they disliked (describing it as *'boring, with nothing to do . . . crap . . . old and dirty and horrible'*).

Informants contrasted the relatively anonymous atmosphere in Sundon Park with the strong sense of local identity which they imagined would exist in a smaller community in a place like Ireland, where one of them had relatives. (*'There in the street, everybody knows everyone. You can walk at 11 pm and feel safe. People are so friendly. Here people are strangers, you don't know half of the street. People keep themselves to themselves.'*)

The **19- to 34-year-olds** also spoke of the lack of any sense of local community in Sundon Park, ascribing this in part to the lack of a community centre. (*'We lack community spirit because there is nowhere to meet or raise funds or organise events.'*) Because many residents had cars, and many preferred to shop in a large supermarket in another ward, few people used the local shops which might otherwise have been a centre of community. (*'It's quite possible to live here, and yet to have every aspect of your life – your work, your shopping – outside of Sundon Park.'*) Again and again people in this group expressed the view that *'Sundon Park, like a lot of places, has become nothing more than a place to live – it is certainly not a community'*. There was much discussion about whether it was possible to have a sense of community in any modern city suburb. People felt that these days the only place where one would find community might be in *'villages'* – *'places in the countryside,* *or the Welsh valleys'* – where there were fewer houses, fewer cars, fewer people, in a smaller and more clearly delineated area – and where people got to know each other's parents and families, inter-married, went to village fetes, discos and so on.

Despite this, they felt that Sundon Park was a fairly pleasant place to live – unremarkable, quiet, friendly enough. On the whole it was safe, apart from occasional vandalising of telephones and bins, burglaries, speeding cars and joy-riders (reference was made to an old man who had recently been knocked down on a pedestrian crossing) – but these were rare occurrences.

There was some debate in this group about the extent to which people wanted to be close to their neighbours, with one informant making an impassioned plea for closer community ties. (*'Wouldn't it be nice to know that your neighbours actually loved you and cared about you? To know that there was actually somebody there, that care extended beyond just if you fell over in the street, coming over and dusting you off, say, you know, but that actually cared about you, cared about your family. Wouldn't that, I mean, I think that would be a nice sort of community?'*). But another felt uneasy about the intrusiveness implied in this vision of community. (*'I think it's quite enough just to know that the neighbours would be there in an emergency. I wouldn't like my neighbours to love me like my mum does. It would be too consuming . . . they'd be in my house all the time, or on the phone. No.'*)

The **35- to 55-year-olds** were the most positive about Sundon Park. They agreed that the area had no distinctive identity or 'feel' about it (*'there is simply nothing here – no community centre – nothing'*). However having said this, they tended to speak very positively about the ward. It was seen as a relatively safe area compared to other parts of Luton. People often regretted their decision to move out of the ward, and came back as soon as they could. The fact that many of residents had been born in the community made for a stability and sense of belonging that they valued highly. (As one woman in her late 30s told us: *'My, my grandmother lived here as well with us, and some of her friends – in their nineties – are still around. When they see me they still say, "Oh, look, there's Maud's little granddaughter", I don't know, I just feel safe here.'*) Even those who had not grown up in the community found it friendly, with people greeting one another in the street.

One flaw in this relatively peaceful community was the problem of badly behaved children – here as in several other focus groups, the example of footballs in gardens was raised. People felt that children often entered people's gardens with inadequate respect for their privacy or their property. (*'For some, their front garden is their little castle, they just don't want people trampling on their flowers . . . but children are not brought up to respect this . . . they should at least knock on the door and ask if they can get their ball back.'*)

Another possible disadvantage was the possibility of gossip and nosiness, particularly for those who lived in small closes, where everyone's comings and goings could be observed. Some found this intolerable, but others felt that physical proximity need not be a problem if it was sensitively managed. (*'I try and greet people in the street but don't ever invite them in.'*)

Children were seen as an important source of local networking. In particular, mothers of small children worked hard to make friends and life for themselves in the neighbourhood. Building community was described as women's work. Men would come and go at night and their wives would fill them in on what was going on. While some men might play snooker with a same-age neighbour after work or gather in garages to help one another with cars, they were the exception rather than the rule. One man commented that he had recently met a neighbour at a street party who had lived in the street for 22 years. (*'I had never seen him before. I am always at work you see.'*) Another man agreed with him. (*'I am out all day and I just come home and want my dinner. But my missus is the local Neighbourhood Watch – she notices every car and person that comes into the close and wonders who it is.'*)

The **55+ year olds** echoed the general sense that there was no sense of local identity in Sundon Park. (*'We have no great attachment to the community – there is nowhere that we can meet to build that up.'*) People commented on how homogeneous the community had been 35 years previously when many of them had moved into newly built houses. Everyone in the community had similar life demands and problems, and were forced to rely on one another for support. (*'In the old days we were all young couples with children, we all had no money, no cars, we all had new houses. In those days we had to help each other out all the time.'*) Furthermore a lot of Sundon Park people had worked or in some way been linked to the Skefco factory in the region. Skefco had had a thriving social club, which had served as something of a community centre until it had been closed down to make way for offices. In those days the community had been much more cohesive. (*'We all went to the local school, parents' meetings, raised money for things, attended local dances. It was different then.'*)

An important feature of life in the old days which had served to bind people was the general lack of money – facing a homogeneous community of young families at a similar developmental stage, as well as relative ethnic and age homogeneity. In comparison, Sundon Park now consisted of such a broad range of people with such a broad range of life demands and problems, that people didn't have much in common as they had in the past. Increasingly diverse community composition together with a decline in 'the art of conversation' had led to a sharp decline in the local identity that had existed when this age group were younger.

While people felt little sense of a Sundon Park identity, they agreed that Sundon Park was a pleasant place, conveniently located for public transport to local hospitals, close to the countryside and open fields which people liked. They regretted that media coverage of recent riots in Marsh Farm estate had given Sundon Park an unjustifiably negative stereotype in the minds of outsiders, and one which was not accurate.

3. Sundon Park: trust

The **15- to 18-year-olds** felt that Sundon Park was relatively safe compared to other areas of Luton. The only time they felt their safety threatened was on Friday and Saturday nights, when big groups of young people hung about on the streets and often harassed passers-by. (*'If you walk by on your own you are bound to get abuse – "Have you got money or a spare cigarette or the time?" or "Why are you giving me dirty looks?"'*) This harassment sometimes had a racialised element. (*'Groups of white kids might take the mick out of black kids and vice versa.'*) They spoke at some length of the problem of bullying, which often began within schools and then spilled over into the streets and parks.

An important trust issue for young people related to gossip, broken confidences and false rumours. In addition they said that there was some peer pressure to take drugs, smoke, drink and start fights – but that this pressure was not particularly strong in Sundon Park (on the whole, Sundon Park teenagers appeared to be more home-bound and less rebellious than their Farley counterparts). Another trust issue related to stealing at school. ('*People steal things to make themselves look big to their friends . . . it takes some guts to steal.*') One also gained 'street credibility' among one's friends by taking risks, defying authority and lying.

Trust between members of different age groups was in short supply, in particular there appeared to be a fair amount of conflict between teenagers, and old people. The issue of footballs in people's gardens was a particularly controversial one. While playing football in the street, it sometimes happened that the ball would bounce into the garden – or even worse the flower beds – of an elderly person (for example '*she told us she had been growing those roses for a year, and now we had broken them with one game*'), and every young person had a story of the resulting unpleasantness (for example '*Our football went into this old lady's garden, and she started mouthing off, so we started mouthing off at her, and she scratched my face – grabbing me when I went to pick up the ball. Later my Mum went and pounded on her door, but she wouldn't open it.*' Another informant spoke of an older woman who had stabbed his football with a kitchen knife: '*Dad shot up there and told her to pay for it. She handed over £15*'). Informants of this age felt many old people in the community were unreasonable, because the street was often the only place to play. ('*Old people are always on the offensive. They blow up at us even when it's only an accident.*' and '*There are always one or two miserable old people in every street – they behave as if they own the street.*')

However, on the whole, such incidents happened fairly infrequently (each young person might be involved in one such incident over the 6-week summer break), and the group concluded that such conflicts were not a new thing. ('*It's been going on for generations, old and young not getting on.*') But they said that they often felt that older people had an unduly negative stereotype of the young. ('*They have a stereotype of us, judge us by what they have seen in the paper about young people rather than from who we are.*') They emphasised that the community stereotype that groups of young people 'meant trouble' was often misplaced, and that most of the young people in Sundon Park public spaces were nice kids with nowhere else to go. ('*Anyone walking past the park and seeing me there probably assume that we are in there trying to cause trouble and we aren't. It's just, you know, that's where all my friends go, I just want to hang around with them and we don't have anywhere else to go.*')

People in the **19- to 34-year-old group** felt that levels of trust in Sundon Park were adequate – it was an area where one could safely leave one's house keys with one's neighbours, for example. The extent to which one could trust young people in the area dominated the discussion. People felt that it was difficult to relate to teenagers, that they were unapproachable and often lacked courtesy. All said that on occasion they had been offended by the behaviour of teenagers, for example swearing in front of small children in the park, or damaging council property. However they were divided as to whether one should openly confront 'offenders' of this sort. Some said that if one was careful not to lose one's temper and to try and address the young people respectfully, one could successfully intervene in such situations. Others said that they would be scared of reprisal ('*they might identify you and later attack your house or your car*').

People felt that the police played an inadequate role in dealing with troublesome young people. They referred to other areas (for example Marsh Farm) where the police played a far more pro-active role in communicating with young people. They felt that the police were only visible in a flurry of sirens or helicopters when an emergency arose – and that a more low profile police presence would do a lot to increase people's sense of security and to deter bored young people out to cause minor trouble. However here people emphasised that the problem in Sundon Park was minor compared to other wards in Luton (here Farley was mentioned specifically as one such problem area).

Those in the **35–55 age group** felt safe on the whole, and relatively relaxed about leaving doors and cars unlocked if one was in the house and small windows open. Keys could be left with neighbours. However one would never let a stranger into the house, and one should be careful of everyone, including children ('*who are nowadays as dangerous as adults*'). People felt that this suspicion of children came from the newspapers and television rather than from their own local experience though.

There was some disagreement regarding whether or not one needed to be careful of large groups of teenagers hanging about outside the shops. Some were very tolerant of them ('*I have lived here for so long I know most of their mothers and fathers*'), but others were more nervous ('*I would always be wary of the children at the shops, I simply don't trust any kids these days*'). They believed that most of the 'problem' young people came from reasonable family backgrounds, but might be led astray by peer pressure. ('*Parents always think their kids are great, that they are goody two-shoes. They never suspect that they might be effing and blinding outside the shops.*') Furthermore there was general agreement that people were too quick to heap negative stereotypes on young people. ('*One is usually pleasantly surprised, when you actually get talking to one of these beings that you cross the road to avoid on a dark night, and he turns out to be a perfectly pleasant young adult.*')

General levels of trust in the community were believed to be undermined by the lack of respect for the police, particularly by some younger people. Group members felt that here parents set a bad example. ('*Children grow up hearing their parents make negative remarks about them . . . the community needs to work together, to work with the police, rather than against them.*')

Older (**55+ age group**) people regretted that, compared to the old days, one had to take care to lock doors and shut windows. These days older people felt reluctant to go out at night because of the gangs of teenagers who hung around the shops, off-licences and takeaways (14- to 15-year-olds). ('*They don't actually do anything to us, but they do often throw bricks through the off-licence windows and they are menacing and we always worry that we might be mugged or something.*') While they felt that crime was not a major problem in the community, they regretted that there was not much more of a police presence to give confidence to older people. ('*Sometimes one hears sirens on the M1, or they flash by along the road after joyriders, or stop at the café for a sausage roll, or you hear a helicopter – but you never see one on the beat.*')

4. Sundon Park: help and support

Young people (**15- to 18-year-olds**) said while their families tended to have good relationships with neighbours, people tended to prioritise and look after themselves and their families rather than looking to neighbours or other community members for the giving or receiving of help and support. ('*No one goes out of their way to look after us, so why should we go out of our way to look after them*' and '*If people have got their own families, they don't think any more about you.*') On the whole they said that people's contact with neighbours tended to be minimal beyond taking in the occasional parcel for one another, or negotiating discussions about who should pay for common fencing – or occasionally baby-sitting for neighbours, or feeding the neighbour's pets or switching on lights when neighbours were away.

The only exception to this casual relationship occurred at times of crisis – and crises often had the spin-off effect of breaking down barriers between neighbours. Helping one another after burglaries was one of the crisis situations that might cement relations between neighbours.

With regard to extending help and support to elderly people, they agreed that this was not always welcomed. ('*Old people are wary of offers of help from us. They think you might want to attack or burgle them. Or else they like to be independent and get all grumpy when you offer to help because they want to do everything themselves.*')

In summary, they concluded that 15- to 18-year-olds in Sundon Park tended to be helpful, sensible and trustworthy. However on the whole they felt '*a bit wary of helping people – we just try and keep ourselves to ourselves*'.

The **19- to 34-year-old group** said that young people with problems tended to get little support or help from local residents. They relied on families as their major support networks, and those who lived far from their families had little emotional or material support. Job centres and the local council were not regarded as helpful, with poorly trained staff and inadequate resources, and local services – such as health services – were poorly organised and frequently difficult to access. One young man spoke eloquently of the series of 'knock-backs' he had had in his year-long attempt to get satisfactory medical help for his wife's still undiagnosed illness. He said that after one 'knock-back' after another, he was becoming increasingly depressed and desperate, and felt that the strain of caring for his still deteriorating wife and two small children single-handed was becoming almost unbearable.

Neighbours varied. They distinguished between three sorts of neighbours: 'naff neighbours' who avoided any contact whatsoever and behaved with a lack of consideration, especially with regard to blaring music; 'Hi and Bye' neighbours who aimed to be polite in a distant way and to avoid offence, but nothing more – and neighbours who were more caring and trustworthy – who would keep an eye on houses when one was away, or help if the children were sick.

The latter type of relationship with neighbours often took years to build up. People contrasted their friendships with long-standing neighbours with tenants of rented houses who came and went without staying long enough 'for us to bond with them'. The development of neighbourly relationships also involved having time to spend in the community on a day-to-day basis. One woman commented that having moved into Sundon Park when she was a full-time worker, she only got to know anyone once she had to take time off to have her first child. (*Otherwise you go to work, you go home, do what you have to do inside the house, and go to work again the next morning.*)

Good neighbourliness also resulted from living in a small and enclosed area – with the close being the ideal setting. Those who lived on the busy main road with the hustle and bustle of activity around the shops and the traffic found it more difficult to develop a sense of local community.

There was some debate about the degree of closeness one should aim for with a neighbour. (*You don't necessarily have to be in and out of each other's houses to be good neighbours. You can be thoughtful of each other and watch out for each other without. People do like to keep to themselves these days. They wouldn't want you to knock on their door, but if you notice something was amiss, they'd quite like you to tell them about it.*) Others preferred to be closer to their neighbours – saying that good neighbourliness meant that one could go into someone's house without knocking and that one's children felt equally comfortable in the neighbours' houses and their own.

People felt that on the whole there was a willingness to 'keep an eye' on elderly neighbours (for example to check that they were all right if they failed to take in their milk on more than one consecutive day), and that most people would help one another in the case of illness or injury. But apart from that there was no great ethic of accepting support. (*People don't like to ask for help, or to accept it when it is on offer.*)

The **35- to 55-year-olds** also regarded a good neighbour as one who was civil and avoided unpleasantness, but nothing more. People said that neighbours took in parcels for one another, and sometimes helped elderly neighbours with things such as cutting the grass, but that one needed to be wary of getting too involved with others in the community. Two reasons were offered for this. Firstly there was a strong resistance to the notion of 'being nosey' or 'interfering'. (*Of course one should be interested in one's family and perhaps one's immediate neighbours and people that you know, but you can't go nosing in on just, sort of, like Joe Bloggs up the road really. He would resent you doing that. He'd think you were playing about if you kept knocking on the door and offering to help.*) Secondly there was a sense that just looking after oneself and one's family was more that a full-time job, and that there simply wasn't time to extend one's energies further. (*People are too busy out trying to make a living and get by to worry about other people really. I mean if you are out 60 hours a week trying to get a living wage together you just haven't got time. It's a bit of a selfish attitude, but you've got no option. It all boils down to the crap wages they are paying at the moment.* *If we was all on £15 an hour and we done 30 hours a week, then perhaps we could look after the old people in the close.*)

Thus, while some people said that they might, for example, offer to do shopping for elderly neighbours occasionally, one needs to be careful not to get drawn into taking too much responsibility for them. (*If elderly people don't have children it's got to be down to social services.*)

Here, as in Farley, there was general agreement that women were better social networkers than men, and that they were better able to access and offer help and support. ('*My circle of women friends – we have all had different problems or been cross or upset, and when we get together we can talk them over, have a laugh, feel so much better.*') Men on the other hand found it difficult to trust people or build deep and sustaining relationships. ('*Men don't form deep relationships very easily. You can go out for a pint with someone or a game of snoooker, but that is as far as it goes.*' '*We men can't allow anyone to think that we can't cope, we keep things to ourselves too much, thinking that this is manly.*')

In speaking of reciprocal help and support, the **55+ age group** expressed concern not to encroach on their families. Older people often had more access to their neighbours than their children. Group members felt supported by their neighbours on the whole. ('*We don't want to be in each other's pockets, but we only have to shout if there's an emergency.*') While they felt that neighbours could be relied on, with so many younger people away at work during the day, often the community felt quite deserted. ('*I fell once in the street at 10 am. There was not a soul about to help me. People will help if they are about, but this is a dead place between 10 and 4.*')

There was a general sense that communities were not as supportive as they had been in the old days, and that there was a growing reluctance by people to get involved in other people's problems and difficulties. ('*People have become very greedy and selfish. Everyone seems to be taken up on their own with no time to consider others.*' '*The world has speeded up so fast, people don't have time for others.*') Growing affluence relative to the past enabled people to be more self-sufficient. ('*Before we didn't have much, we had to lend each other things – not everyone had shovels, spades, lawnmowers as they have today. Now people have got it all, they don't need other people.*')

5. Sundon Park: attitudes to local politics

The **15- to 18-year-old group** said that they knew 'nothing' about politics ('*at our age we can't be bothered with that*'), however the discussion suggested that they knew more about national politics than their Farley counterparts. They knew that politicians were concerned with issues such as tax and employment for example, and had a clear sense of the fact that politicians should represent the people that had elected them. They were already cynical about them. ('*Politics never works*', '*they try and change things without it ever happening*', '*they promise too much, but it's all in theory*', '*they can't be trusted.*')

The **19- to 34-year-old group** expressed little faith in their ability to influence the political process at a local level – people were doubtful about the calibre of local councillors for example ('*they scrape the bottom of the barrel to find people to stand for election*'). While there was a feeling that the council had achieved some things – improving the local park, painting lamp-posts, working towards university status for the Luton poly and so on, their chief preoccupation was the community's long-standing failure to get a community centre. The local residents' and tenants' associations had long waged an unsuccessful campaign in this regard.

Some commented that the only local people available to be active in grassroots politics were the elderly, who often lacked the skills and energy to make things happen, or the unemployed, who often lacked the confidence. Employed people were too busy making ends meet. (As one employed young man said: '*Someone like me could never get involved – I am never at home, all my time is spent out trying to make ends meet.*') Another – unemployed – young man said that people like himself lacked the 'self-belief' to get involved in creating local networks and organising around community issues. ('*People like me just lack self-belief. I'm sure there are thousands of people like me in the area that could work well for the community, people that are at home all day, have lots of time, could contribute to things like this and achieve a lot, but who's there to encourage us? If you have never been in a career how do you ever start to believe you can achieve anything?*')

Another informant said that the reason why local people had been so unsuccessful in lobbying for the community's needs was because there was no local identity. ('*It's because there is no, I suppose, there's no heart to, to, to the Sundon Park community, then it's, it's very difficult to, to get things, to get things moving.*')

There was general agreement about the importance of voting, but doubt as to whether politicians achieved the idealistic goal of representing the interests of their constituencies. However citizens also had an obligation to try and do something more than simply complaining about unmet community needs. ('*Too many people complain without taking the time or opportunity to influence things. We have become a nation of complainers rather than pro-active people who care about the communities we live in.*')

The **35- to 55 year old group** were extremely resentful about their perception that because the community did not have any conspicuous problems, it was continually passed over by local government when it came to allocating funding for community resources. They felt that one of the reasons for the lack of problems was that parents kept an eye on their children, and also because many of the houses were privately owned – which '*attracted a better sort of person*' and which also gave people an investment in making the community a pleasant place to be. People were extremely negative about the council ('*useless*'), and in particular resentment about the lack of facilities and groups in the area (ranging from the unmet need for a community centre, to mums' and tots' groups and playgroups for children), with people ascribing this to the fact that because the ward did not have any problems, it was simply ignored by local politicians. ('*They get all this grief in Marsh Farm, so they think, "we'll build them a sports centre, quiet them down". We have no problems here, most parents keep their kids in. At Marsh Farm the buses come by every five minutes. Here you wait up to an hour.*') People felt cynical about the fact that the only time they saw their counsellors was immediately prior to an election ('*you get a whole dozen of them knocking on your door*').

They also felt that the grassroots local community was apathetic and ineffective in its attempts to work towards community improvements. The local residents' association was seen as toothless. ('*We have all been to residents' association meetings, and nothing's really come of it.*'). People were divided about the extent to which community members were committed to local affairs. Some said they were apathetic. ('*Everyone moans about what goes on in Sundon Park, but nobody turns up.*') Others said that there was some level of civic commitment among the citizens (they pointed to both the church hall and the Evergreen club for pensioners as the result of community initiatives), but the council failed to provide the leadership necessary to channel this effectively. ('*Some people here* are *community minded, but they get no help or encouragement from the council.*')

The **55+ age group** engaged in heated discussion about the extent to which citizens could influence local conditions in the community (for example as they had with complaints about the local peanut factory which resulted in noise and a bad smell). Some said that citizens had great potential power through writing letters and making phone calls to the council on controversial issues which they were too apathetic to exercise. One man in the group said that he frequently phoned the town hall to complain about things, only to be told that nothing could be done because he was the only person complaining ('*If things are wrong here, it's 90 per cent our fault*'). Others felt that it was a waste of time ('*we tried to stop them building the factory there – there was a big meeting, but we were just bulldozed – they went to the government who forced the decision through*'). Others felt that at their age they lacked the vigour to take up local issues. ('*In the past we all joined in various protests about things, but now as time has gone by transport becomes more difficult, our health isn't that good, how can we participate to any great degree?*')

They were sceptical about the value of voting. ('*All that politicians do is slag each other off, like children – they fill up their nests and move on – just there to look after themselves.*') They felt that the council tended to be unresponsive to requests or complaints ('*You often have to make yourself unpleasant to get things done.*') Council staff were often employed part-time and there was little sense of continuity in trying to follow up complaints or requests. However, on the whole Sundon Park residents were uninterested in politics, possibly because they were largely '*contented with our own little Sundon Park world*'.

6. Sundon Park: significant formal and informal group memberships

The one facility for young people was the youth club (the Rendez) which opened on Wednesday and Friday nights. This seems to be a popular and useful community service, but young people wished it could be open on Saturdays and Sundays. This age group expressed the need for more clubs and activities for people of their own age. Their wish list of activities included a sports club, a drama group and a discotheque. A few had had slight involvement in school charity functions, but not all. When asked about church groupings they were adamant that they had no appeal for this age group. ('*It's not considered "cool" . . . our friends would tease us, call us "Bible-bashers".*')

The **19- to 34-year-old group** referred to the Dawsons social club – where men often like to meet over a drink at lunch time, and which sometimes organised discos for young people. They also referred to the local pub, The Favourite, as a pleasant place to go, particularly in summer when one could have lunch in the garden. However they said that many of their age group were either stuck at home with children, out working long hours to make ends meet, or unemployed with no money for leisure pursuits. Other pleasant meeting places were the library, the local shops and the school gates. ('*Here you all natter to one another, yap away, it doesn't matter that you hardly know who* *anyone is.'*) The children's clinic where babies were weighed was also a useful place for building community contacts. The local Anglican church had lost its popularity with a new vicar who was not as attractive to families as the previous one. Thus, for example, he had refused to allow the popular Mothers' Union mother and toddler group to continue to use the church hall for their meetings which had caused some degree of bad feeling.

People were mixed in their desire for more opportunities for community involvement. Unemployed people said that they would be happy to become more involved in community projects. Others said that they would prefer more passive involvement – such as attending fetes on the day, provided they did not have to help organise them. There was a strong need for more activities for children – dances, fetes, face painting and so on. People also spoke of successes they had had going down to the park and starting a game of rounders with a group of children. Here, the teenagers who were hanging about invariably approached and asked if they could join in. The consensus was much more community-building could be done in a relatively informal way if people took more initiative in this regard.

The **35- to 55-year-olds** also spoke of the need for more informal groupings in the ward. They said that the Catholic and Baptist churches were well attended, and provided some sort of associational life for their own members (clubs, playgroups, Brownies and so on), but for non-church members there was not much. They too regretted the new Anglican vicar's decision to stop the Mothers' Union from using the church hall for mother and toddler groups, they said that there was a need for more playgroups for children, they felt the community would benefit from a swimming pool, a snooker hall and table tennis facilities. In response to complaints about the lack of a swimming pool, other group members protested that the high school pool had in fact been open for public use at one stage, but closed after lack of support. This prompted a discussion about how there were so many rules and regulations governing the opening of public facilities that it often made it unfeasible for schools to make their facilities available to the public out of school hours. Thus for example, a school making its swimming pool available to the public would be burdened with so much liability and red tape – insurance, lifeguards and so on – that it could seldom afford to take on this responsibility. In response to complaints about the lack of a snooker hall, some group members reminded others that the Rendez (the youth club attached to the school) did in fact have snooker, but there was general agreement that few people know about what was available. Furthermore people said that a youth club was not a congenial place for people in their 30s and 40s. The local pub, The Favourite, was criticised for being rowdy, and having too many little children running about.

There was some debate about who might take responsibility for the community activities which were lacking. It appeared that such responsibilities always seemed to fall on the same small group of people. The problem was to mobilise support from a wider group.

The **55+-year-olds** described Sundon Park as the 'Cinderella of Luton', in terms of the lack of community centre and other facilities. They complained that community members did not have access to the '*lovely school with a pool that the community raised money for, sports facilities there too, but we are not allowed to use these*'. The only exception here was that certain people had access to the school for two hours a week to play bowls. There was a general feeling that the council tended to provide more facilities for those on problem council estates. People felt there was too little sense of local community to sustain the organising of more local voluntary groups. They regretted the fact that the local Townswomen's Guild which had thrived for about 15 years had eventually disbanded due to dwindling interest. People felt that there was a lot of apathy among Sundon Park citizens. ('*People have tried to organise things over the years, tenants' and residents' associations and the like, but they all eventually drop off because people weren't interested and nothing got done.*')

They said that they would greatly value the opportunity for more community activity. When asked why they were not pro-active in creating this, they replied that they had all done so at various times of their lives – running a football club for the children when their sons were of school age, or other such activities. However these activities had often fizzled out because only a small group of people had been prepared to organise them. ('*Only certain people would help. Others were happy for you to have their children at your activity, but they didn't want to help.*') Apart from the lack of a broad enough base of people who were motivated to sustain such activities, these days younger people were too busy with their lives to put effort into community activities. ('*A lot of them don't work in the community, a lot of industry here has upped and vanished, no one is around to organise things for the children, they are all too busy and too far away making ends meet.*')

Older people felt reluctant to go to the local pub (The Favourite). They felt the pub was a bit like a 'youth club'. They said the community would benefit from a 'nice family pub' where all ages felt equally welcome. The pub was no longer a place to chat as it had been in the past, with the music being so loud. People referred to pub league dominoes as one activity available to those who had transport – this was held out of Sundon Park. Local activities included the Evergreen club, the Catholic club where one could go for a drink, and the day centre for geriatrics (members of our particular group felt that they were not yet 'that old').

Even those activities that did exist didn't always serve the role of integrating people into the community. People said that attending local yoga or evening classes could be extremely lonely and alienating if one didn't take a friend with one. ('*People at these things are very groupy. They arrive with their friends and stay with their friends.*')

There was some debate about who should take responsibility for the poor facilities and lack of voluntary associations in the area. Some felt the lack was the result of citizen apathy. ('*We complain, but what do we do to put it right?*') Others felt it was due to council apathy. ('*We pay them – the council should take more responsibility.*')

Summary: subjective perceptions of social capital in Sundon Park

All age groups agreed that there was no sense of *local identity or belongingness* in Sundon Park. Residents said the area was 'simply a place to live', with no local 'heart' or 'spirit'. They ascribed this chiefly to the lack of a community centre and a dearth of local associational life or leisure activities. In addition, a growing number of people worked and shopped outside of the ward. Despite this, people felt the area was a pleasant enough place to live – relatively safe, reasonably friendly, with access to the city centre and to open fields. Elderly people said that the community spirit they had enjoyed thirty years previously (when the majority of them had moved into the area as young couples with small children) had dwindled, as the community became less homogeneous – particularly in relation to a much broader age range, and people having far more variable incomes than they had in the past.

Levels of *trust* among community members were said to be adequate for comfortable living. People generally felt safe, able to leave keys with neighbours and so on. Perceived levels of crime were low. The only area in which levels of trust were compromised related to conflicts between younger and older members of the community. People spoke, for example, of the occasional unpleasantness which resulted from children's footballs going into elderly householders' cherished flower beds. Furthermore, all four age groups, but particularly older people, felt threatened by groups of teenagers (14- to 15-year-olds) who hung about in large groups in the street, parks, and outside the shops. However these groups represented a minority of the young people in the community rather than a majority. On the whole, crime was not seen as a major problem, although several groups said that quality of life in the area would be improved through a more conspicuous police presence in the community.

With regard to *help and support*, people felt that one could rely on other community members in emergencies. However people were wary about the extent to which one should involve oneself in the lives of other community members, and offered four reasons for this wariness. The first two reasons related to the importance of not interfering in other people's lives, and the importance of being independent. 'Being nosey' was seen as an unpardonable social offence. This made people reluctant to show too close an interest in other people's affairs. Furthermore there appeared to be strong sanctions on people to 'look after themselves' or 'cope on their own' rather than asking for help. Thus people with problems were said to be 'too proud' to ask for help, and often tended to battle on alone. The third reason for not taking too close an interest in other community members' problems was a practical one. People said the heavy demands of looking after one's own immediate family and of making a living meant that they lacked the time and energy to involve themselves in the lives of those who were not family or close friends. Fourthly there was evidence for an individualistic ethic – a sense that one's main responsibility was to oneself, one's family and close friends, and that those who fell out of the circle were not one's responsibility. Other community members who lacked close family and friends to care for them were seen as the responsibility of the social services.

The networks of help and support that did exist in Sundon Park appeared to be strong between mothers with small children, who spent the most time at home. There was general agreement that women were better at creating and accessing the existing social support networks than men – firstly because they were more in touch with their emotions, and hence more willing to admit vulnerability, and secondly because they had better social skills for networking. Men were less involved in existing social networks, and accessed them through their wives.

With regard to *attitudes to the local council*, people felt that the local council failed to represent the community's needs adequately. There was great resentment that because the Sundon Park community had no conspicuous problems it was continually passed over, with resources always being channelled more strongly towards problem communities. People felt extremely resentful about the lack of community facilities, despite the fact that tenants' and residents' associations had long attempted to motivate for these.

With regard to their attitudes to the *potential power of citizens* to influence the shape and quality of community life, there was some debate about the extent to which this lack was the result of apathetic citizenry, incompetent grassroots citizen representation or unmotivated council representation. Some said that citizens of Sundon Park were apathetic and did not do enough to lobby for community improvements. Others said that citizens had tried to lobby but often lacked the skill and knowledge to do so effectively. Others said that the lack of facilities was all the fault of the council – that there was latent grassroots community-mindedness, but that the council had failed in its leadership role of tapping into this and transforming it into effective action. The common denominator in all these arguments was the belief that citizens ought to involve themselves in lobbying for community improvements, and that, with the right combination of council and grassroots activism, the community could in principle be improved. These views were underpinned by a far more active notion of citizenry as well as a far greater belief in the potential power of local government to deliver good things than was manifest in the Farley focus groups.

Perceptions of social capital in Farley and Sundon Park: similarities and differences

The final section of this chapter provides a thumbnail overview of differences in focus group informants' perceptions of levels of social capital in Farley and Sundon Park, according to Putnam's dimensions of local identity, trust, reciprocal help and support, perceptions of local government and citizen-power.

With regard to *local identity*, conceptualised in terms of (i) perception of the local community as a pleasant place to live; and (ii) a sense of local belongingness, there were some similarities and some differences. Both Sundon Park and Farley residents in the three younger age groups regarded their communities as pleasant places – with both wards having easy access to the city centre, yet at the same time bordering on open countryside, with a solid core of long-standing residents to provide a sense of continuity, as well as enough private home-owners (compared to council tenants) to provide a sense of permanence. On the whole, houses and gardens tended to be well cared for (although there was some discontent in both wards about the council's tardiness in maintaining certain of its properties).

There were strong differences in the accounts that focus groups gave of the sense of local belongingness in each of the wards. Farley residents spoke of a strong and positive sense of local identity – as opposed to Sundon Park residents who said that the ward lacked any kind of 'local heart or spirit' and was nothing more than 'a place to live'. Farley residents spoke of a ward where houses were laid out in small clearly delineated areas, with community being particularly strong in the shorter streets, closes and cul-de-sacs; they spoke of a 'nice atmosphere' where during the day people would greet one another in the streets and compliment gardeners on their handiwork as they walked past. During the day, Farley's streets and public places were occupied by pedestrians, children (often playing football) and the ubiquitous gangs of teenagers 'hanging around'. (This was a daytime atmosphere – at night adults tended to be more wary about crime and stay indoors as much as possible, although the teenagers did not appear to feel this concern.) Sundon Park residents tended not to inhabit the streets and public spaces as much as their Farley counterparts. The majority of teenagers tended to conduct their lives within the confines of their own and friends' homes rather than in the streets and public spaces. Many Sundon Park car owners preferred to drive to supermarkets outside of the ward to do their shopping. Many people worked outside of the ward, leaving at 7 am and returning at 7 pm, and staying indoors for the remainder of the time. During the day parts of Sundon Park appeared completely deserted – never the case in Farley. While Farley was considered a very good place to stay by teenagers, with strong street-based peer networks, Sundon Park teenagers found their community dull and adult-focused, with few activities or amenities for young people. Young people in Sundon Park tended to be more home-bound than those in Farley, playing a far more muted role in community spaces and community life than their Farley counterparts who were far more aggressive in colonising public spaces and in making their presence felt in the youth-dominated street culture of the community at large.

The only exception to the positive sense of local identity in Farley was found among the 55+ age group. Here, their views were very similar to those of the 55+ age group in Sundon Park, namely that the communities were not as pleasant as they had been in 'the old days' (twenty or so years ago).* They said that in both areas in those days the communities had been relatively homogeneous, with large numbers of young couples with little money, no cars and small children, community members had had more in common, and because they shared similar life problems there was much more communication, and much more of a culture of caring and support. Nowadays they felt that the increasing heterogeneity of their communities – in terms of age, ethnicity and income – had fragmented the relatively easy unity and reciprocity that had dominated in the past. Older people in both communities also commented that there was a greater turnover of residents in the highly mobile modern culture. Their personal experience had suggested to them that community links were built up over years, and that it was difficult for new residents to integrate in a meaningful way unless they stayed in the community for some time.

As has already been said, young people in Farley were much more conspicuous and assertive in their colonisation of public spaces, and in a range of attention-seeking behaviours. Even those teenagers who were most resentful of the negative image of their age group in the community conceded that it was not completely without foundation. All the other age groups in Farley felt that large groups of teenagers intimidated other community members – in minor ways such as blocking pavements, using bad language, asking passers-by for cigarettes, and in more serious ways such as throwing bricks through shop windows, or verbally taunting passers-by.

*Clearly the reinvention of 'the good old days' when everything was better is a feature of the narratives of old people the world over, who idealise the past as a strategy for dealing with their growing loss of health, vigour and control in worlds where old age is increasingly devalued. Against this background, reference to 'the old days' must be seen as a rhetorical device, rather than an accurate depiction of life in Luton thirty years ago. Rhetorical devices of this nature serve to provide useful insights into elderly people's subjective perceptions of the present – and should be seen in this light, rather than being regarded as accurate descriptions of the past. This point is taken up in Chapter 4.

The general tension felt towards these groups of young people was one of the reasons for Farley residents reporting much lower levels of interpersonal *trust* than Sundon Park. Older people were deeply mistrustful of teenagers and younger adults, saying this mistrust affected the quality of their day-to-day lives. Younger Farley people were resentful of their allegedly inaccurately negative image, saying that it made them feel simultaneously rejected and angry. (While inter-generational tensions were also referred to by the Sundon Park focus group members, these were of a far less serious nature.) But in both areas, adults said that they lacked confidence to challenge young people who might be misbehaving in the streets, for fear of recrimination – and that in some sense this reluctance meant that the communities did not provide adequate guidance or structure to young people testing the limits of adult tolerance. This view was ironically also expressed by Farley teenagers, who said that despite the pleasure and peer recognition to be gained from being rebellious, now that they were reaching the age where they should enter the formal labour market, they felt that the community had not given them the type of guidance and support that would have best prepared them for the discipline of the workplace. Apart from the inter-generational issue, Farley residents also expressed a greater wariness of strangers than those in Sundon Park – saying that one could never be sure that a stranger was not at worst a criminal or at best trying to take advantage of you in some way.

With regard to trust, the views of the 55+ age group in both wards were again similar: with older people commenting on the relative anonymity of community life compared to the past – in 'the old days' if one knew one family member, one could trust them all, compared to these days where one tended to form relationships with isolated individuals rather than necessarily getting to know their whole family.

With regard to the issue of *reciprocal help and support* among community members, people distinguished between emergency and non-emergency situations, with the latter referring to practical help (for example loan of tools, accepting parcels from delivery-men, borrowing small amounts of sugar) and day-to-day emotional support. Here informants in both focus groups raised similar themes: unwillingness to offer help through reluctance to be seen to be 'interfering' or 'nosey'; not having the time or energy to take on other people's problems; and because of an ethos of prioritising one's own family over other community members. People were also often reluctant to ask for help due to a sense of pride and independence which led many to hide their difficulties from others as much as possible. However, despite similarities in the two wards over these issues, Sundon Park people went to greater lengths to emphasise an individualistic ethic in a community where energies and priorities tended to be located within the confines of people's homes as opposed to Farley, where people's lives and concerns tended to spill out into the street far more freely. Thus, while informants from both wards felt that the community served as an excellent safety net in times of crisis, Sundon Park residents tended to aim for a civil but distant relationship with other community members on a day-to-day basis – as opposed to Farley residents whose lives seemed to be more intertwined with those of their neighbours, the children in the street, and so on. (This point will be refined somewhat in the discussion of social networks in Chapters 5, 6 and 7.)

Attitudes to local government and citizen power were also superficially similar in many respects in the two wards. While people took an abstract interest in local affairs, read community newspapers and so on, this did not translate into community activism, or even the widespread use of community facilities and institutions. People in both wards complained about inadequate community facilities, particularly those for young people; expressed the view that the local council had scant interest in and a poor understanding of community needs; felt that the local tenants' and residents' associations were largely toothless and ineffectual; thought that on the whole local citizens were apathetic, preferring complaining rather than acting to improve things, but said that even those few who did try and involve themselves in grassroots activities aimed at community improvement generally became despondent at their lack of success and gave up. However, despite these differences at the superficial level, Sundon Park residents had a greater belief in the potential of local government to serve the community, and the potential of ordinary people to bring about community improvements provided they were given adequate support from the council and other community members. This point was substantiated very strongly in the in-depth interview analysis (see Chapter 7). Sundon Park people were more critical of the local authority than their Farley counterparts; Sundon Park residents had a history of successful community fund-raising activities (for example building the local church hall) – compared to Farley residents who only had stories of failed petitions and fund-raising that had never had any results they were aware of. Sundon Park had a large voluntary residents' association (with 500 members) which was initiated and run by local people, as opposed to Farley which only had council-run ones.

In terms of *formal and informal group memberships*, in both communities there did seem to be some leisure activities and voluntary groupings, but interest and participation in these appeared to be low. Farley residents referred to a range of community groups and activities (church groups, Scouts, the Evergreen club, aerobics classes) but tended to be dismissive of these. Farley appeared to have a far greater range of council-organised and council-funded activities. However, ironically, while people in Sundon Park complained extremely vociferously about lack of facilities, during the course of the focus groups it emerged that there were indeed a range of facilities that people were not aware of – and that a number of initiatives (for example opening the school pool to the public, the Mothers' Union which had been strong for many years) had been closed due to lack of interest. A major difference between the two areas was the lack of a community centre in Sundon Park, with Sundon Park residents citing this as a major reason for the poor 'community spirit' in the ward. Facilities that did exist in Sundon Park were mostly privately owned and administered (the Dawsons social club, the local pub, local church groupings).

Concluding comment

In short, our pilot study has suggested that while Farley (our low-health ward) had more local *facilities* as well as a greater sense of local *identity* than Sundon Park (two essential features of social capital as defined by Putnam), compared to Sundon Park, it lacked two other essential features of social capital, that is *trust* between community members and confidence in their power as *active citizens* – both of which were relatively high in Sundon Park, our high-health ward.

The in-depth interview analysis reported in Chapters 4 and 5 support these findings, as well as clarify and refine them in various respects, leading us to put forward the hypothesis that certain aspects of social capital (in particular trust and perceived citizen-power) might be more relevant to health than others (for example local identity).

With regard to local facilities we will suggest that while these could potentially play an essential role in generating social capital in local communities, this depends on the circumstances under which they are provided. Despite the fact that the council has clearly put greater effort into establishing local facilities and activities in Farley than Sundon Park, these facilities have not served to enhance social capital in the ward. Firstly they are not perceived as widely accessible or desirable by many residents, so that they are not regarded as positive and empowering resources by the majority of Farley people. In other words, the provision of local facilities is not enough – these need to resonate with the social identities and expressed needs of community members if they are to have maximum benefit as community resources. Secondly Farley residents have a passive client–provider relationship to many of these facilities and services, without being aware of any channels whereby they might influence the way in which such facilities and services are provided.

With regard to local identity, as will be discussed at length in later chapters, while levels of ward-based identity were lower in Sundon Park than Farley, Sundon Park residents had access to a *wider* range of social networks that were *less locally based* than those of Farley. Recent research into the role played by social networks in the lives of unemployed people suggests that people might derive more benefit from a geographically wide-ranging array of social networks (of the kind available to people in Sundon Park) than a geographically restricted and relatively narrow set of social ties (of the kind that dominated in Farley) (Perri 6, 1997). Our pilot research results will lead us to suggest that Perri 6's views on the relative benefits of different social networking patterns might fruitfully be imported into the field of health research – in the interests of developing and investigating our hypothesis that different patterns of networking might be associated with different health outcomes.

4. Trust and local identity: the quality of community relationships in the past and present

Chapters 4 to 7 report on the findings of the in-depth interview study. In this chapter particular attention is given to people's subjective experiences of community life in the two Luton wards, paying particular attention to the issues of trust, reciprocity and local identity. In Chapters 5–7, focusing on social networks, the phenomenon of civic engagement will be explored in more detail.

In-depth interview methodology

Open-ended semi-structured interviews were conducted with 37 informants, who constituted a sub-sample of those survey informants randomly selected for Leonardi's parallel survey study (Leonardi *et al.*, in preparation). At the end of each survey interview, survey informants in the two lower socioeconomic status wards – Farley and Sundon Park – were asked if they were interested in taking part in a three-hour interview in their homes. Thereafter people were selected in such a way as to have equal numbers of men and women, spread across the 16–34, 35–55 and 55+ age groups. Appendix A categorises each interviewee in terms of age, marital status, employment, number in house, number of children, number of years in the ward.*†

*Leonardi's survey sample (from which the in-depth interview sample was selected) was overwhelmingly white. As a result except for one person (I11, who described himself as African Caribbean), all of our in-depth

The interview topic guide (see Appendix B) contained questions relating to each informant's life history, their health history (where health was broadly conceptualised in terms of physical, mental and social wellbeing), their perceptions of community life in their ward, and what they considered to be their most significant formal and informal networks, as well as factors which tended to help or hinder involvement in these networks. A decision was made to use a long and broad-ranging topic schedule and to devote three hours to each interview because, at this early stage of the history of health and social capital research in the UK, very little is known about the networks and relationships constituting social capital in local communities. We believed that in this context it would be premature to cast our research net too narrowly. Interview participants were encouraged to speak freely on whatever associations the questions elicited, and the interviewers placed as few constraints on people as possible.

The aim of the interviews was to complement the focus group material – which by its nature tends to consist of fairly broad and sweeping generalisations – with a more detailed and nuanced account of the forms of social capital present in the two communities. Interview analysis took place in two stages. Although each interview covered all the topics listed in the interview schedule, the open-ended nature of the interviews meant that our information of interest emerged in different forms and contexts and at different stages of each of the interviews. For this reason stage one of the data analysis involved sorting the large amount of data (1600 pages) into broad content categories. The NUD*ST qualitative software package – a tool for exploring the meanings of large amounts of unstructured data – was used to sort the interview material into 12 major categories ('the old days' associational life, types of networks, types of support, accessing networks, community action, views on survey questions, concepts of community, community strengths and weaknesses, perceptions of health, community events, feedback) which were further sub-divided into 115 sub-categories (see Appendix C for an account of the coding frame that was used at this stage). The coding process separated information according to ward and gender (that is four separate NUD*IST files were created for Farley women, Farley men, Sundon Park women and Sundon Park men).

interview respondents were white (English, Irish, Scots and Welsh in origin). This is clearly a severe limitation of our study, given the large south Asian and African-Caribbean populations in Luton. However, taking ethnicity into account would have been too complex in a pilot study whose aim was to generate conceptual tools. A follow-up study is currently in the planning phase to examine social capital in a wider range of groupings in the Luton region.

†In the text of the report people will be referred to by their 'informant number', as agreed in negotiations about anonymity prior to each interview. Thus I1 is the first person we interviewed, I2 the second and so on. In addition to citing their informant numbers in the text, people will be referred to as FM (Farley Man), FW (Farley Woman), SW (Sundon Park Woman) and SM (Sundon Park Man). Thus (I1, FM) is the first person we interviewed, and he is a man from Farley.

Stage two of interview analysis involved total immersion in the coded data for a number of weeks. Successive attempts to 'reduce' the data to a manageable number of core categories – which adequately reflected the dominant themes underlying informants' accounts of their experiences and perceptions of community – resulted in the final categorisation of the interview data within the following broad categories:

I. Subjective perceptions of community. (As will be discussed in this chapter, the central theme emerging here was that of a perceived decline in the quality of community relationships, based on present–past comparisons.)

Ia. Types of community relationships that have 'declined'
- trust
- neighbourliness
- reciprocity.

Ib. Reason for this 'decline' in positive community relationships
- decline in common social identity
- changing living conditions
- increasingly heterogeneous community composition
- youth-related issues.

II. Types of networks and associations constituting social capital in these wards
- informal face-to-face networks of relatives and friends
- voluntary groupings (leisure, hobbies, personal development)
- formal and informal community groups and networks.

Chapters 4 to 7 provide a critical overview of the material in the light of the categories outlined above. The aims in these chapters will be threefold: firstly to provide an analytical overview of the material, with illustrative quotations from the interviews; secondly, where relevant, to highlight similarities and differences in the accounts of social capital in our two wards of interest; and thirdly to discuss the extent to which informants' accounts of social capital are consistent with the account of social capital provided by Putnam (1993a).

Here again we must re-emphasise the nature of the claims we seek to make on the basis of these data. The size and nature of our sample restrict our ability to claim that the information presented here is a reliable and valid account of community life in Farley or Sundon Park. Our goal has been to conduct some of the conceptual groundwork for our hypothesis that Putnam's notion of social capital is a useful tool for health promotion in this country – through exploring the extent to which Putnam's definition of social capital resonates with the daily experience of residents of our wards of interest. Given its depth and richness, the material we have collected provides a robust starting point for such a goal. It provides a basis for our attempt to highlight the types of local issues, networks and processes which might exist as a resource for those concerned with planning and evaluating local health promotional policies and programmes – that seek to promote the existence of health-enabling local environments.

Subjective perceptions of 'community', past and present

> The woman leaning over her gate with her pinny on having a natter with someone, like everyone knew everyone else. You must have heard it no end of times, people saying they never used to lock their doors, but that's how it was. (I14, SM)

When asked to give an account of their perceptions of 'community' in their residential ward, informants drew on the past as an idealised reference point in pointing to what they experienced as a decline in local community. A large research literature bemoans the inaccuracy of nostalgic, utopian reconstructions of community life in 'the past', emphasising that such reconstructions are often historically inaccurate and that despite people's romanticised memories, life in these allegedly ideal communities was often oppressively hierarchical (particularly with regard to gender and class) and unpleasant (for example Crow and Allen, 1994; Demaine and Entwhistle, 1996). Such authors also emphasise that people have, throughout history and in a range of cultures and contexts, bemoaned the decline of phenomena such as trust and inter-generational respect over the passage of recent time, and imply that such nostalgia is simply part and parcel of how people negotiate the stress of social change which is an inevitable feature of the human condition (for example Pahl, 1995, 1996). While we would not disagree with Pahl's claims regarding the historical and geographical frequency of unfavourable past–present comparisons, we disagree with the implication that as such they have little interest as data for social scientific investigations of contemporary community life. The *reasons* given for these comparisons are inevitably historically and geographically specific, and as such can serve as useful sources of information about people's subjective experience of contemporary community life.

Furthermore, much has been written about the unusual rapidity of social change at the historically specific moment of the late twentieth century. Writers such as Hall (1992) and Giddens (1990) highlight the implications of what they describe as a historically extraordinary situation for ordinary people struggling to create coherent social identities in local and global worlds which are increasingly fractured, unstable and unpredictable.

Hall points to a 'crisis in identity' resulting from the rapidity of social change:

> . . . the old identities which stabilised the social world for so long are in decline, giving rise to new identities and fragmenting the modern individual as a unified subject. The so-called 'crisis in identity' is seen as part of a wider process of change which is dislocating of the central structures and processes of modern societies and undermining the frameworks which gave individuals stable anchorage in the social world. (Hall, 1992, p. 274)

Characterising the process of transition from a 'traditional' to a 'post-traditional society', Giddens (1990) comments that in a 'traditional' society (as opposed to a 'modern' one) people are able to insert activities and experiences into the continuity of past, present and future, which is structured by recurrent social practices. This is not the case in post-traditional societies, which are constantly changing in nature. Individuals are constantly dislocated/disembedded in a process that unhinges the stable identities of the past, and continually opens up the possibility of new articulations of the self. Under such conditions people are constantly having to construct and reconstruct their sense of self, in the light of changing social circumstances.

Implicit in our interview data were signs of the impact that these processes of dislocation have had on community life in our two wards of interest – particularly in terms of the way in which they have had an impact on the interlocking phenomena of *local identity* and *trust*. We will argue that one of the key factors distinguishing Farley (our low-health community) and Sundon Park (our high-health community) was the way in which Sundon Park people have succeeded in creating networks and identities that transcend the growing limitations of small local communities of the type that Farley residents still aspire to. Such small local communities are no longer sustainable because their existence and functioning were premised on their relatively homogeneous and stable composition and their relatively predictable nature – conditions that are decreasingly feasible in the late twentieth century. In these small local communities, where far more people were personally known to one another and had far more in common than the communities of today, it was easier for people to sustain a sense of common identity, as well as trust. It was possible to have stronger consensus regarding norms of acceptable behaviour within a relatively closed and restrictive social system which, because of its (relative) stability and homogeneity, was able to regulate itself in a fairly predictable way. One of our goals in these qualitative chapters will be to trace the adaptations that Sundon Park people have made to changing social circumstances.

The historical accuracy of people's accounts of the past is not at issue in this chapter. Past–present comparisons of the quality of community life are of interest to us for two reasons:

1. The first reason relates to one of our key concerns in this report namely 'community' as a source of strain or source of support. Past–present comparisons are of interest to us regardless of their historical accuracy because they were often used by interview participants as a rhetorical device for pointing to those aspects of community life which they found negative, stressful or disempowering – clearly important information for a study which seeks to understand those aspects of community that promote or hinder health.
2. The second reason relates to a theme that will be taken up in this and the next chapters, that is the extent to which Putnam's view of social capital resonates with the experience of local community members. People's romanticised accounts of the quality of community relationships in the idealised past (in terms of trust, reciprocity and neighbourliness) were remarkably consistent with certain aspects of Putnam's characterisation of social capital. It was through attention to people's explanations for why such ideal communities could no longer exist in the contemporary world that we derived important information about ways in which the quality and form of contemporary community networks are different from Putnam's account of community life in a number of important ways.

Having argued that accounts of 'the old days' are important sources of data for our particular purposes, we will take care to use the phrase in quotation marks to highlight the constructed and possibly idealised nature of the 'past' that people spoke of.

Compared to Putnam's concept of the civic community with its emphasis on dense and interlocking community networks in the voluntary, state and interpersonal spheres, our informants' subjective past–present accounts of community related almost exclusively to interpersonal relationships between community members, with only minimal reference to voluntary associations of any kind, and no reference at all to any aspect of local or national government.

Thematic analysis of people's accounts of community life in the past and present suggested that they clustered around the four categories of: *trust, local identity, neighbourliness* and *reciprocal help and support*. The reasons people offered for what they perceived as a decline in these four 'quality of community relationships' categories fell under three headings:
- changing living and working conditions (where reference was made to issues of transport/mobility, shopping, pace of life/time, range of leisure pursuits);
- changing community composition (where the past was characterised in terms of relative homogeneity in relation to age, socioeconomic status, ethnicity, stability of housing tenure, homebound women);
- the changing position of young people in communities (where distinctions were made in terms of levels of communal caring/responsibility, discipline and boundaries, range of pressures on young people).

On the whole, people's responses were remarkably similar across both gender and ward, and for this reason, in the earlier part of this chapter informants' responses will be presented with no particular reference to these variables. Towards the end of the chapter different trends across ward and gender will be highlighted.

These four categories were presented as ideals that should be aspired to, and people generally expressed regret, occasionally even guilt, that contemporary life made it difficult for them to 'preserve' these ideals. However they were clear that given the demands of contemporary life these ideals were no longer feasible or realistic. Each is now discussed in turn.

Symptoms of decline in 'community'

Trust

As was the case in the focus groups the definition of trust implicit in the interviews was a state where people could rely on others to act in their best interests. Best interests included: (i) treating them with an attitude of general respect and tolerance, and more specifically (ii) respecting their privacy and good reputation in the community – both through keeping confidences and avoiding spreading harmful gossip, and (iii) respecting their physical safety and the safety of their property.

In the interviews, the issue of trust emerged in relation to three categories of people: people one knew personally, strangers and politicians. However, the focus groups as well as Chapter 7 highlight the minor role that politicians play in people's views of contemporary community life, and they did not feature at all in past–present comparisons.

Respect and tolerance

This issue emerged mainly in relation to inter-generational relationships, particularly in relation to young people and the elderly – with both groups feeling that they were not adequately valued by the community at large. This point emerged repeatedly in the focus group chapter, and is dealt with at length in the sections on 'Divisions and conflicts' and 'The role of children and teenagers' below.

Gossip

While there was general agreement that changing social conditions had led to a decline in all the other elements of trust, people were divided in their views on gossip. Some said it had always been a problem. Speaking of his childhood, I29 said:

> There was an inquisitive nosiness among neighbours – the curtains fluttering you know – liking to know everyone's business. They would all tut-tut, it was everyone wanting to know everything about everyone else, and not wanting anyone to know about them. (I29, FM)

Some people suggested that if anything there was less gossip now than in the past, particularly with people more open-minded about issues regarding single motherhood and teenage pregnancies. However others believed that the situation had got worse with regard to gossip:

> People here are very two-faced. They don't keep confidences. Mum had friends that she could really trust, it's harder now. The estate is bigger and with more people we are not as close. Also there seems to be a lot of jealousy when some have more than others. (I4, FW)

Another said that levels of nosiness had always been high, but that in the past they had not generated as much antagonism as they would today:

> People have always been nosey, but people didn't respond as aggressively as they do now. Before, if you were staring at someone they might have turned around and said 'Seen enough?' or some such remark that would cause you to go bright red, but it wasn't said with the aggression that people seem to have these days. (I5, FM)

Safety from crime

In relation to this aspect of trust, the first dimension was safety from criminal or anti-social elements (where anti-social elements consisted of mischievous children or teenagers who caused real trouble, but could not be held totally responsible for their actions due to their immaturity). The second dimension was safety of one's property, and the physical safety of oneself and one's family. Both were believed to have increased considerably in the recent past:

> The crime situation has got worse over the past ten years. It's a combination of drugs, unemployment and nothing to do. I think its drug-related, an awful lot of youngsters with no access to work, in order to get a few shillings for drugs they will mug someone. (I1, FM)

> I was born after World War II. Things were different then. There seemed to be more community spirit. People are more suspicious now, crimes of violence are up, there is a whole new set of crimes, graffiti spraying, muggings. When I was a kid I knew that if I did something

like that and got caught, I would get a whack around the head. There's also a more confrontational atmosphere. There were always old fogeys who would wave their sticks at you, but that aggression now between the old fogeys and the kids in the street seems much greater. (I5, FM)

With regard to personal safety, the three main fears were muggings, burglaries and what were referred to as 'sexual perverts':

When I was growing up, we could go out on the street, not having to worry about dirty old men or anything like that. When my kids were growing up, we had a couple of those around here – tried to interfere with one of my kids once. (I28, FM)

With regard to safety of one's property, burglaries or thefts were referred to as a growing problem in both wards. However, while in Sundon Park people feared burglaries by strangers, in Farley people sometimes even feared thefts by people known to them personally:

With a new neighbour, at one time you would go over, talk to them, say come in and have a cup of tea while your stuff is being unloaded. Not any more. You let them in your house, and the next thing you know, it's been robbed. (I28, FM)

Some older people spoke of the decline of the good old-fashioned virtue of honesty, which they believed was less widespread than it had been in the past:

People were more trusting and honest when I was younger. If I was in the club and found a £20 note in the toilet, I would go around to each bloke and ask if he had lost the money. Nowadays someone would have picked it up and you would never see it again. (I25, SM)

Children's freedom of movement

This relatively generalised trust of other community members meant that in the past children had far more freedom to roam around the neighbourhood – a situation that was often described in lyrical terms:

Where we grew up it was over the hills and far away freedom, literally cross the road and disappear and come back when the sun went down and there was no parental worry, no weirdos to threaten us. (I29, FM)

It was much easier for my parents to let me go out and play – in those days we were quite an insular grouping, parents knew all the older children, it was much safer, we knew more people. I would never let my children go out on their own. These days there are far more people who might harm them. Parents having to worry about sick-minded people and drug abuse and smoking by young children. (I22,FW)

My grandmother would park my pram in the forest while she went to do her charring. You couldn't leave a child in the forest today. I had a wonderful childhood – free to roam quite safely alone in the bluebell wood all day. (I16, FW)

We had a lovely childhood. Money was short, but we were happy. It was all woods and cornfields around here, it was so safe, as children we could have stayed out in the woods until 12 midnight without any harm coming to us. (I25, SM)

There were frequent references to today's 'nutters' who might harm children.

Neighbourliness

In their accounts of the idealised past, high levels of trust went hand in hand with a culture of neighbourliness. While people felt that neighbours could still be relied on to provide *help and support in emergency situations* (such as accident, illness or fire) in the contemporary community, they were unanimous in their view that there had been a decline in the culture of *positive social exchange between neighbours*. This social exchange took a number of forms. The first was the easy access that neighbours allegedly had to one another's houses – such as the custom by women of 'nipping in and out of each other's houses for tea' (I28, FM). As I39 (SM) said, 'there was never a front door or a back door locked, they were always in each other's pockets in those days'.

Customs practised by both men and women involved chatting over the gate or the fence, and greeting people in the street, whether or not you knew them:

> You don't have 'neighbours' any more in the sense we used to understand it. No one will come in and say: 'Oh I have just nipped in for a cup of tea and see how you are'. If they see you outside they might talk, but that's that. There's no 'neighbourhood'. You see people walk by, you know if you say hallo to them they look at you as if 'What does he want?' You know a lot of people have run the Asians down, but I always find, even if I don't know them, when they are going by the house they smile, say hallo. But the white people, basically even me now, I've got to the stage where unless I know someone, I don't talk to them. (I28, FM)

In her interview, I10 (SW) spoke at length of her hurt and bewilderment at her new young neighbour's reluctance to return her welcoming greetings in the street:

> There is a new young couple with small children across the road – if we are out there chatting and say 'Hallo, how are you' as she walks past, she just nods her head and keeps walking. Youngsters these days are brought up not to trust people, they think if you greet them you have

an ulterior motive. These days so many people live far away from their families, and everybody needs a Nan figure or a Mum figure — and a lot of the new young couples in this area don't have that. She could come and knock on my door if one of her children was screaming and she didn't know what was the matter, and I would look after the other children while she sorted the problem out. (I10, SW)

For men an important dimension of neighbourliness in 'the old days' had involved interacting with other local men in the community pub:

There is no one around here I could suggest going out for a drink. I largely keep to myself and live my own life and let others live theirs. The rare occasion I go to the Parrot [*the local pub*], I go in, people turn around as I walk in the door, and then just turn away. I buy my drink from the bar and sit down on my own. (I5, FM)*

Such statements contrasted with people's references to the pub as their own fathers' major social network.

Hand in hand with this decline in neighbourliness was a decline in what were called 'social graces' (I10, SW) between local people:

Things have changed in a very short time. Even fifteen years ago I would never have thought of not going to the back of a queue at a bus stop. Nowadays people stand in a shop doorway and as the bus is coming down the road suddenly rush forward and take the front of the queue. (I5, FM)

References were often made to what people perceived as increased levels of aggression which might intrude unexpectedly into the most minor encounter:

I would only smile at someone in the street if I knew them, smiling at a stranger might earn you a mouthful of abuse. (I6, SW)

People these days are different in their attitudes – more arrogant, more bombastic. Sometimes I daren't even speak to people, we all keep far more to ourselves now. (I25, SM)

The lack of neighbourliness meant that compared to the old days, people had relatively little knowledge about one another's lives:

People keep to themselves. The old boy across the road died some time ago, and we only found out recently. (I29, FM)

---

*Italicised words within quotations denote comments inserted by the author.

Not everyone regretted the decline of the 'dropping in' culture however:

> I automatically call to the neighbours if I have a problem, but I am not in everybody's pocket. At the end of the day my home is my home, and people are welcome to pop in, but not too often. It'd drive me scatty to have people dropping in day in and day out. I am too busy to be honest, rushing around after the kids, to have time to sit in people's houses drinking coffee. (I34, SW)

As was the case in the focus group, however, the issue of maintaining social boundaries between neighbours was only mentioned by Sundon Park informants, who devoted much detail to outlining a complex set of norms which they observed in relating to others in the community:

> It is important not to interfere . . . Interfering is insisting you will do something to help even if you get the vibes that they don't really want it. It's difficult. You have to read people's body language. I mean, usually if you were to offer to do something for somebody they would say no straightaway, even if they really wanted help because they wouldn't want to be seen to be so keen. And you would have to insist a bit, and then if they gave way it would be OK. But if they really said they were adamant, and you went on and on – that would be too much. (I6, SW)

Reciprocal help and support

The neighbourliness of 'the old days' was not confined to congenial social companionship. It also had a practical dimension ranging from minor acts of practical support to major shared responsibilities on a long-term basis. At the minor level, with relatively restricted shopping opportunities, borrowing small amounts of food was common:

> The door wasn't locked, and if say Mrs M upstairs wanted to borrow some milk or a bit of sugar, she'd pull the door open and go 'cooee' and come in. (I5, FM)

Under some circumstances, loans of money or sharing of bigger items such as shoes or clothing took place:

> If you couldn't afford something they would say: 'Well I have got this pair of shoes that will fit you'. And if anybody had a baby, they would say: 'Why don't you use this or that?' It was a smaller community and we helped each other through. (I32, FM)

> The neighbours were good, very helpful. If you were short of bread and butter you had no problem getting it. Or if you were short of a few bob to get something, they would help you out and then you would just pay them back as you were going along. (I26, SM)

Emotional support was also frequently on offer:

> If you were in trouble the neighbours were always there with advice and help. Like a bereavement in the family and you don't know what to do. So the neighbours would come in and some went down and did little jobs for you, and got things moving for you. If one of us was ill and had to go to hospital. And there was no transport in those days. (I1, FM)

In cases of illness or death, neighbouring women would take on even bigger tasks and responsibilities for neighbours who were in trouble or needed help:

> When I was a kid and my gran [*who brought him up*] was ill, the neighbour would come in and make sure us kids were up, breakfast, dressed and ready for school. You don't get that any more. (I28, FM)

> Several doors away the wife died of cancer. Well men didn't really know how to bring children up in those days, and in that sense the kids were brought up by the neighbourhood. People did look out for other people. (I29, FM)

Several people linked declining reciprocal help and support to a culture of individualism which they traced to eighteen years of Thatcherism:

> The Thatcher bandwagon – own your own home, look after yourself. It sharpened up a dog-eat-dog approach, and people started caring less and less for anyone else. It was, 'I'm all right Jack and bugger you'. The overall outcome was less social responsibility – with the emphasis on the betterment of the individual only. (I29, FM)

A number of informants contrasted community in the present day with the days where people would help one another with no expectation of reward:

> People don't help each other out and I think that's terrible. I do lots of favours for people in my workshop and people moan at me for helping others out. My daughter says, 'You must be daft, doing all that . . .' but years ago that's how it was. You helped me, I helped you, that's the way things used to go on. But people don't do that today. Everybody wants some reward for what they do. (I13, SM)

Causes of decline in 'community'

Informants cited a number of reasons for what they perceived as a decline of the old-fashioned community virtues of trust, neighbourliness and reciprocity. These included changing living conditions, an increasingly heterogeneous community composition and youth-related issues. Each of these factors contributed to undermine the sense of common identity which had been the common factor underlying each of these three civic virtues.

Local identity

Again and again people referred to the strong sense of local identity that had prevailed 'in the past', which manifested itself in a range of contexts:

> In those days a funeral would begin from the house. The pavement would be a mass of flowers. (I21, FW)

> In those days everyone in the street was 'Auntie'. There was Auntie Sheila, and Auntie Bet and Auntie this and Auntie that. All the neighbours were Aunties because Mum was always with them. And everybody just helped everybody. (I4, FW)

There were many references to the way in which World War II had served to unite people:

> When my parents were young, the war had just finished, and there was a much higher sense of community after the nearness of tragedy. It brought people together. During the war there were lots of really awful things that happened and it brought people together and the aftermath of that feeling lasted for many years afterwards. (I6, SW)

To a certain extent this identity was based on first-hand acquaintance with the neighbours:

> Everybody used to know each other, more or less, and if you didn't know the names you knew the faces. This led to help and trusting. (I25, SM)

> In those days you knew everybody in every house, so you heard their good news, you heard their bad news, so you could help straightaway, people would always help. (I1, FM)

The fact that people were known to each other was associated with a climate of mutual concern and shared responsibilities:

> Everybody knew you – if you had an accident in the street there was always someone who knew you straightaway; if your children strayed too far from home or misbehaved, there was always someone who would recognise them, and it would get back to you. If there was a stranger in the close people would keep an eye out to see if he was acting suspiciously. (I21, FW)

But even if they were not known to one another, there was not the suspicion of strangers and fear of crime that existed today:

> In the old days you could knock on any door, ask to use the toilet, or for a glass of water. Nowadays people would think you had come to rob them. People could go outside and leave the back door open, not any more, crime has increased so much. (I21, FW)

Two factors combined to increase this sense of community identity and trust: firstly, as has been mentioned, that in 'the old days' many more people were known to one another. Secondly, even if people were not known to each other, the composition of the community was such that one could assume a common identity – even with strangers – on the basis of assumed commonalities. This easy sense of commonality was partly a function of *working and living conditions* which threw people together far more at the local level than current working and living conditions today, which (we will argue later) push people into social networks that are at once much narrower (immediate family and household) and much wider (beyond the boundaries of the residential ward) than the old-fashioned communities or neighbourhoods that people spoke of. It was also a function of people's perception that the *composition of communities* in the two wards had once been far more homogeneous than is the case today. Each of these factors is now discussed in turn.

Living and working conditions

Living and working conditions in the mythical past conspired to promote local community identity through factors which restricted people's movements outside the area, and provided them with more opportunities to get to know one another. Firstly communities in this past were perceived to have been *smaller* than they are today, with the growing population of contemporary communities leading to greater anonymity:

> Before, when Sundon Park was smaller, everyone knew each other. (I25, SM, 75 years)

Secondly people's movements had been restricted because *transport* facilities had been less well developed:

> I never got to know my cousins because we lived in different parts of town. In those days if you left the street you lived in, you felt as if you were going to foreign places. You never left your area unless it was a special occasion. (I1, FM)

> With no cars, people couldn't get out. You were constantly near to each other. (I30, FW)

> Dad's friends were all local people who lived nearby. In those days one didn't go too far, because it was always on foot. (I16, FW)

> When I was growing up in the early 60s not many had cars. You travelled by public transport if you had to. You went to school and then you came home. It wasn't often that you went anywhere else to see people. (I22, FW)

Because people had limited access to areas beyond their immediate living spaces, residential proximity was more likely to be a key factor in defining one's social circle. When close friends moved to another geographical area they were replaced by new locals:

> My parents' friends always lived in the area. Those who moved out – there was always someone to take their place – we mostly stayed in the street, and didn't go away from the street very often to visit. Nearly every aspect of our lives took place in that street. (I21, FW)

Because people walked around a lot, there were far more opportunities for contact with neighbours:

> We would bump into one another, and quickly go around to one another's houses. (I8, FW)

> In those days everyone knew everyone because you walked everywhere – I still don't drive and when I walk out I usually bump into a dozen people I know. My husband, who drives, would go out and not recognise a soul. (I17, SW)

> It's a quiet close – people just get in their cars and go, there's no neighbourliness any more. People hardly walk to the end of the drive. I can hear my neighbours next door all the time, but I probably don't see them more than once every two months to speak to. We used to all help one another run errands, 'I'm going to the shop, can I get you anything?', now people just jump in their cars. (I17, SW)

It was through ongoing casual contact with neighbours on pavements in streets and closes that opportunities for mutual help and support arose:

> I think we are the last generation that will have cared for their old people. My friend's 80-year-old mother lives in the street, and I will walk by and ask her if I can bring anything back from the shop for her, but the younger people all have their cars – they drive out of their drives and don't even notice who they are passing in the street. (I17, SW)

It was not just relative restrictions on one's daily movements that enhanced opportunity for community-building, but also the fact that people tended to live in particular residential areas for *longer* than they do today – this was the third feature people highlighted in explaining the decline in the strength of local identities:

> There's not the neighbourly feel there used to be. People don't stay in the same place for so long. They used to move in and stay here until they died. (I24, FW)

I10 (SW) described contemporary Sundon Park as a 'transit community':

Years ago, we were all in the same position, tiny children, very little money. All the mums were home, so that helped us to get to know each other and, as the children grew, the community grew also. But as the children grew up, lots of parents moved off to bigger houses, or smaller houses, or smarter houses, several emigrated to Australia, and only left a few of us here. This street turned out to have been a stepping-off place for families – and then more young families moved in – but the new families are a different generation – we don't have anything in common to bond over. (I10, SW, 65)

There are only six or eight of us original families left in the close. They just go and take with them the sense of community we built up over years. New people can't fill their place, there needs to be continuity for a community to exist. These days everything is disjointed. (I10, SW, 65)

There used to be a strong sense of community here, but not so much now. The old families have moved away, young people have moved in with tiny children – it's a bit sad, they don't ever seem to want to stop and have a chat. Perhaps they might think we are busybodies – I don't know, but I feel it's very sad. (I10, SW, 65)

In short, the relatively reduced transport and mobility in the past meant that people had many more opportunities to get to know one another.

The fourth aspect of living conditions 'in the old days' that threw local people together was *shopping*. Frequent nostalgic references were made to the relatively small and personal shops of the old days, which provided ample opportunities for interpersonal contact:

We knew all the shopkeepers, I could tell you their names, there was relationship between us all, not like today with big supermarkets. A dairy shop, a fish and chip shop, a toy shop, a cafeteria where you chatted the girls up. The cobbler's shop. These days there's no cobbler's shop, just thousand of shoes being churned out. A sweet shop, a betting shop and pubs. Now people go to the big shops, the big supermarkets. This changes things. You used to meet people there and get the local gossip and talk, stand talking to the shopkeeper. (I9, FM)

Small shops did not only provide opportunities for getting to know people, they also provided the opportunities for the building up of trusting relationships between local shopkeepers and their customers:

Sundon Park was a nice place to grow up, everyone was friendly, in the shops you would get your shopping and pay for it all at the end of the week – you don't get anything like that now. (I14, SM)

The fact that shops are now open for longer times and that virtually everyone has

TRUST AND LOCAL IDENTITY **85**

refrigerators and freezers, means that these days people do not need to borrow so much from one another:

> In those times, shops were different. Milk was brought by the milkman, so very few shops had milk available if you ran out. You had to depend on the neighbours in that situation. Now the shops are open until 8 pm, and they sell anything you might run short of. (I5, FM)

> I don't need a little shop nearby any more. I just buy milk and put it in the freezer. (I3, SW)

Furthermore many modern people preferred to shop in large supermarkets outside their wards:

> Shopping patterns have changed, with out-of-town shopping areas which I use. I like their amenities, but I can see how they have changed communities. (I22, FW)

Fifthly, it was not just increased opportunities for contact that led to more opportunities for community-building. The pace of life was *slower* in 'the old days', which also provided increased opportunity for social contact:

> Now everything's so quick. You'd meet other people in the shops, have a good old gas. Gossip, everyone knew everyone and everybody spoke and had a wee time to talk. There wasn't such a rush. The rushy society means that people, if you go anywhere, it's like woosh, woosh, woosh, people get there, quick in, quick out – community simply doesn't happen in that sense any more. Nowadays if you're in a supermarket queue, the woman in front won't say: 'It's a nice day', will she? She will say, 'I wish that bloody person would hurry up and get out of here'. Years ago there was time to talk to people. (I9, FM)

> There is no time for community spirit these days. It's busy now. Before people were in and out of each other's houses. Nowadays we are all so busy working, bringing up the kids, paying our mortgages, running our cars. (I26, SM, 53)

> In this day and age there is too much to do. People feel they haven't got time to stand around and chat. (I14, SM)

Increased pressures of this sort also meant that, for example, men had less time to spend in the pub together:

> When I was a kid, all the men used to go to the pub, it was an all male thing. Half the community would turn up to watch the boxing on a 9-inch screen. The atmosphere is different now. They just rush in, drink quickly and go home. We used to only have two drinks in a night but you would spend the whole evening there, playing darts, or skittles or cards. (I35, SM)

Sixthly, as time passed, the number of *women* going out to work had increased dramatically. Given that women were widely acknowledged to play the central role in social network creation and maintenance (see Chapter 5 for further discussion of this point), their increasing absence was an important reason for the decline in local community identity:

> The nucleus of community starts when mothers are at home so they obviously talk to each other, and this spreads from that – whereas nowadays more women go out to work early, come home from work late, and don't meet anyone. You don't have women spending half an hour at the local shops as they used to – so where do people have the chance to meet? (I29, FM)

Now that there were more women at work, and more people travelling further to their workplaces, the locality was often deserted during the day. Compared to women, men did far less networking, and their networks were often established out of the home and street, in local pubs and clubs:

> In those days we knew everyone in the neighbourhood. My wife used to know them all from the neighbourhood and I used to know them from using the Skefco club. (I25, SM)

Finally, contemporary society also offered increased opportunities for *leisure* activities, often outside the community, so that people depended less on the company of local people for their entertainment:

> Partly it's the way we have changed in life that there's less community, there are so many other things to do. Go to the theatre, play golf, so many other things that weren't there years ago, cars, things changing, the more freedom we've got, the less community there will be. The objects we have got in life stop people, help them to be more lazy, do nothing for themselves except watch TV. (I9, FM)

The decline in community was ascribed not only to changing living conditions which resulted in less opportunities for contact, but also to changing community composition which meant that people had increasingly less basis for a place-based local identity.

Community composition

Perceived homogeneity of 'the old days'

Even when there was not first-hand acquaintance with community members, people said it had been easier to have a sense of common identity with local people in the days when Luton was a more homogeneous community. This was one of the reasons for a stronger sense of cohesiveness that had existed in the remembered communities of their parents' and grandparents' generations.

The first common denominator that united people in working-class local communities in the past was their relatively similar *lack of affluence*. Many people expressed the view that in the past twenty years or so, there was a greater general level of affluence – as well as more conspicuous income differences – within working-class neighbourhoods. Poverty was often referred to as a common bond which had served to unite people – both through creating a sense of common plight, and also because in situations of scarcity neighbours were more likely to turn to one another out of need:

> Life has changed since my parents' day, people have got so much more these days. They were quite poor and helped each other. (I40, SW)

They said that poverty had created a 'need' in the community, with residents frequently being forced to rely on one another for help and support:

> In the old days, people were a lot closer. They had to be. The need was there. (I21, FW)

> It was a lovely community when we arrived here. We were all young, had no money, but we would help each other out, they were lovely days. (I7, FW)

Reference was also made to the increasingly mixed *ethnic* composition of the community. People said that differences in culture and background made the community feel fractured and disjointed in a way it had not when the bulk of its inhabitants had been white and English:

> Nowadays neighbours don't talk to one another. We are so cosmopolitan: English, Irish, Scottish. You've got every nationality up here. It's all split up. And all the children that we knew moved out, and have gone afield. So it's a completely different estate really . . . There are Turks living around here, women that's got yashmaks on, Arabs walking about with their shirts hanging out, loads of Irish people. (I32, FM)

People felt that the lack of integration of the increasingly diverse ethnic strands of the community was an important reason for the perceived decline of community identity and cohesion:

> There is less community spirit nowadays. We are too cosmopolitan. There are too many foreigners, we are a big mix of races, all with our own cultures and that's why community has changed. (I26, SM)

In this relatively homogeneous society, there had been more of a sense that local people had things to talk about and *common interests*:

They used to talk about hats and stuff like that – and also about the Luton football club, that was the main thing. In the 40s or pre-war, Luton was much smaller – if you went down to the football ground they were all supporters, in black-and-white colours and they were proud of the town. How many are proud of it now? (I32, FM)

After the war we were all ex-service people here. You couldn't get a house unless you were ex-service. People were pleased the war was over. They didn't even see a banana or an orange when the war was on, kids were excited – it was peaceful like. And so they all seemed to be happy. Top of the garden there, Sunday nights, we used to, when it was sunny and quite warm, we used to stop up there and it got dark and we were still talking over the fences. (I32, FM)

In comparison to the 'good old days' when people had common identities which led to high levels of trust, reciprocity and neighbourliness, contemporary communities were characterised by a range of community divisions and conflicting interests which according to informants undermined the likelihood of the easy community interactions of the past.

Divisions and conflicts in contemporary community life

The most striking example of community divisions was restricted to the Sundon Park interviews – divisions between residents of the Marsh Farm *tower blocks* at one end of the Sundon Park ward, and residents of houses or smaller flats outside of the Marsh Farm area. I11, one of the two tower block residents in our sample, referred to the strength of some residents' feeling of alienation from the wider local community:

They should knock these flats down. It will start to break down some of the separations the flats maintain ['us' v. 'them' in the Sundon Park community]. I'm not as ready to go as some people, but so many people constantly say 'I want to leave the flats, I want to get out'. (I11)

People are brought up to be aware of their personal wealth, and if they live in a house which is a certain size and pay a mortgage they tend to look differently on other members of the community who aren't as well off. You'll get people who live within eyeshot of these flats who would never take the stigma of saying they live in Marsh Farm, they tell people they live in Sundon Park. And in this way they are, like, dividing the community, making it into different areas. (I11)

Having referred to the stigma with which tower block dwellers were regarded in the general community, I11 himself sought to draw a clear distinction between himself and other residents:

I understand the people around here, but don't have much in common with them. I am a motivated person, but around here I see more unmotivated people than I see motivated people. You can tell that they are not doing anything in particular with their lives. They moan about rubbish, about where they live, as opposed to getting on with life. (I11)

Sundon Park residents living outside the tower block area confirmed the low regard in which people held the tower block residents:

I would say that you can trust people if you know them or if they live in your neighbourhood. I would be less likely to trust someone on Marsh Farm. (I33, SW)

Marsh Farm, it's nasty up there with the riots and everything. Up here it's a lot quieter, everyone says hallo and gets on. There is not so much noise. You can move around freely, feel safer. (I38, SM)

Frequently stigmatised in the Farley interviews were the so-called *problem families* – council tenants who had been relocated into the ward after causing trouble in their previous ward of residence:

This used to be the best estate in Luton, but it's going downhill fast with all the problem families being moved in. It's a false economy – to take people away from a rough area, put them in a good area, so they can destroy the good area too. (I21, FW)

Reference has already been made to *ethnicity* as a factor that people said undermined community cohesion and identity. In our particular sample, people generally spoke reasonably positively of different ethnic groups – in particular Asian families were frequently singled out for mention as caring and considerate neighbours. However, some people believed that the wide range of differences between some groups and others undermined the possibility of a common identity. Thus for example I11, the only black person in our in-depth interview sample, said that cultural differences would have made it unlikely that his Caribbean grandmother would have turned to her white neighbours for support in bringing up her orphaned grandchildren despite the fact that they were on good terms:

People don't understand each other's cultures . . . My grandmother, she had no support apart from us children and she had a lot on her hands in that household. Except to go to church, she didn't ever leave the home to visit friends or anything. There were neighbours and they were friendly – but they came from a different culture. She wouldn't have been able to talk openly to them, or share her problems at the same level. It was in church where she went twice on a Sunday and once during the week that she met with other black people who were her support system I suppose. (I11)

Older informants ascribed part of their sense of community fragmentation to perceived lack of sympathy or understanding for *elderly people*:

> Now you have two classes of citizens in Sundon Park – the older ones like me, I know them all, one or two of us dying every day – and they ask 'How are you?' and all that, and then the new younger ones who just don't care. (I15, SM, aged 76 years)

> Now the young ones can't be bothered with us old ones – they keep to themselves more – there is a definite split between us. If I needed help I would turn to someone of my own age group. I would feel more comfortable asking them, and feel I could trust them the most. (I7, FW, aged 76 years)

Another source of perceived lack of common identity was the distinction that some informants made between *council and private tenants*. Several informants who owned their homes drew a strong distinction between private home owners and council tenants:

> I feel this estate is like a council dumping ground for the type of people you don't want to have next door to you. People who actually own the houses tend to make an effort to look after them, but every now and then someone moves in and you have wrecked cars in bits at the side of the road . . . (I5, FM)

> You are getting all these people coming in from the outside, being put in the council estates, and it's changing the place. In this street you have two private houses, and then two council houses and then two private houses. The private people get all the hassle from the unruly kids. What you are seeing more and more around here is two respectable houses, two unruly houses, two respectable houses, two unruly houses. Council tenants should be put on an estate of their own. (I25, FM)

The most frequently referred to community split was that between unruly children and teenagers on the one hand and the rest of the community on the other. This is the topic of the next section.

Perceptions of the negative role of children and teenagers in undermining positive community relationships

Featuring centrally in the interviews were people's views that children and young people often behaved in ways that led to conflict and lack of trust in the community. The focus group chapter has already highlighted this view, as well as the perception of the 15–18 age group that they had an unjustifiably negative image in the community. They said they were aware that their street-based leisure activities were often regarded as unduly intrusive of communal public space, but that they could hardly be blamed for this, given the lack of community facilities and activities for people of their age group.

In the interviews, adults' attitudes to what we will refer to as the 'youth problem' varied from sympathetic to hostile. The predominant response was one of sympathy for young people, with people saying that their lives were more difficult than those of previous generations – in terms of new pressures, fewer employment opportunities, as well as what was perceived as declining social support from families and the community in general. According to accounts of the interview participants, a range of circumstances combined to suggest that children and teenagers were not being given adequate support, or being socialised in the life skills which older people felt were essential resources for responsible citizenship. These included loosening constraints, increased pressures and inadequate community facilities and activities for young people.

Firstly people commented that contemporary *parents* showed varying levels of support and responsibility towards their offspring:

> Some people are being brought up where their parents care for them; some, their parents aren't really bothered about what their children do. One of my mates, he can come and go whenever he wants, he lazes around, stays in bed, his mom is not really bothered. She should be encouraging him to go out and look for a job and that. My Mum encourages me to work hard, get better grades, more chance of a better job, think of the future. (I12, FM, 16 years old)

They contrasted this situation clearly with 'the old days' where parents exercised far greater control over their children's behaviour, with force if necessary:

> The older generation weren't as liberal with their kids as younger people are these days. My grandmother who brought me up would make efforts to safeguard me from certain things – mainly to do with going out late. Today you see kids out at 10 pm walking in groups. I just wasn't allowed to do that. (I11, SM, 30 years old)

> Though my father loved us, there was fear, which I think was a good thing. Smacking never did me any harm, and I have grown up into a well-mannered nice person and respectful of older people. (I6, SW, 35 years old)

Financial pressures were one reason given for this situation – often making it necessary for both parents to work, and leaving them inadequate time and energy for their offspring:

> People haven't got time – too busy doing their own thing, they just haven't time for strangers – or even for their own children. They come home exhausted in the evening and just want a bit of peace and quiet. There's no one to show the kids what's right and wrong. Schools are too

lenient. The whole structure has broken down. For the sake of the kids the government should try and help families so both parents don't have to work. (I28, FM)

One important tradition which was less frequently adhered to in families was the family meal:

> Parents don't make enough opportunities to communicate with their children. It's not to do with more mothers working – when I was young and working we had a tradition that the whole family had tea together every day at 6.30 pm – sitting in the kitchen and not in front of the TV. Especially if children have had a bad day at school – you are much more likely to discover if they are worried or upset if you have a regular time of general family conversation every day. I think spending time with children does have an impact on the community – the time I spent with mine made them into stable children, and I do believe they now contribute something as adults. (I10, SW)

Because nowadays extended families often lived over a greater geographical area and had less contact with one another than they might have done in the past, children often grew up without a sense of family history or continuity behind them, as well as lacking in the life skills that one automatically picked up growing up in an extended family:

> What's missing in youngsters' lives is a lack of tradition – the community changes so quickly, people don't have as much contact with their families – my daughter makes a point of telling her children what Nan used to do – it's a very precious thing to know where you have come from. The younger generation don't have enough of that. (I10, SW)

> With less contact between members of extended families, children have less experience of life – like they go into marriage without having had role models of people successfully solving relationship problems for example. (I3, SW)

People implied that today's children were not being armed with the social customs and insights which had served previous generations as useful life resources. Furthermore their socialisation no longer bred into them a sense of communal responsibility or reciprocity:

> In my younger days we had to help, digging in the garden, doing odd jobs that your parents asked you to do. Today they get too much given to them for nothing, and don't expect to have to give anything in return. My grandson refuses to help me with little things in my workshop, but as soon as he wants something fixed, he immediately demands that I do it. There seems to be so little give-and-take in the way he is brought up. (I13, SM)

Many informants referred to parents who appeared to have no control over their children's behaviour at all:

Young mothers don't keep an eye on their children any more – they let them destroy things, e.g. my neighbour's children keep jumping in my hedge. When our children were small we didn't allow that. Especially the unmarried mothers don't seem to be able to cope with their children – so they open the door, tell them to go out and play, and let the children get on with it. (I7, FW)

It was not only contemporary parents who were failing to give children the secure boundaries that people felt were necessary for the development of responsible citizenship. Young people were also seen to be disadvantaged by the decline of consistent and *overlapping sources of discipline and authority* which had characterised life in 'the old days'. Communities in the idealised past were characterised by overlapping networks (family, neighbours, school, police, courts) which people felt had once worked far more consistently and harmoniously in containing and guiding young people away from problem behaviours. These structures had overlapped so neatly because communities had been characterised by clear consensual norms regarding what was considered acceptable behaviour by youngsters, and adults throughout the community could act to discipline children secure in the knowledge that their actions would be supported by the children's parents:

The community police in our village, if you did wrong he would clip your ear hole and send you home. And he'd know what shift your Dad was on and have a word with him on the way home, and you'd get a clip around the ear hole from your Dad too. (I39, SM)

Mum and Dad's friends would look after me, or look out for me, and if I or my sister were out late or got into trouble, there was a warning 'I'll tell your mum and dad if you are not careful'. It was a nice sense of security to have. When you feel that other people are keeping an eye on you, you don't have to worry so much about things. The kids these days have too many pressures. (I14, SM)

These days those attempting to discipline children were no longer guaranteed the support or thanks of their parents:

These days the teachers punish children, e.g. with extra homework and the parent will think nothing of storming up to school and saying 'what the hell do you think you are doing?' – half the kids around here get no discipline at all. (I5, FM)

Some people were scared to discipline other people's children for fear of retaliation or unpleasantness from the children themselves:

At school [*where she had worked as a dinner lady*] I have seen children doing something they shouldn't and automatically say: 'Should you be up that tree?' and they would come down – and only afterwards I would think 'well perhaps I shouldn't have said that, you know' – they know

> who I am, they know where I live, and they might retaliate . . . by throwing rubbish in your drive, or stones at your door – as some children do. (I10, SW)

> A year ago a child was hit by a car here going around the corner on his bike on the wrong side of the road – I went rushing out, I thought the child was dead. Since then I have tried to warn children doing the same thing, but all I get for my trouble is a mouthful of abuse. (I16, FW)

Not only were there external constraints in the form of authority figures. The children had also regulated themselves:

> It never entered our heads to go and break a window or pull someone's garden apart. (I30, FW)

The authority of traditional figures had declined, and without this and the threat of punishment, there was little to deter young people from causing trouble. This was not the case in 'the old days':

> You knew you would get punished, so you didn't do it. If you saw someone else doing wrong you kept well away because you knew that there would be trouble. (I28, FM)

> The police had far greater powers. They put the fear of God into the youngsters – now the young just wave two fingers at the police. (I21, FW)

> Authority has been taken away from teachers. Children are not given the structure they need. (I16, FW)

Furthermore some people felt the *criminal justice system* was letting young people down. I14 was the doting father of an only child, a small boy, and he worried about the fact that too little was done to keep children on the straight and narrow:

> A lot of children get into trouble and because of their age they can't get prosecuted, they just get warned and let off, there's no deterrent. And the worry is that your own son will get caught up in that. (I14, SM)

Several informants commented that it was important for young people to be contained by a social system which made them take responsibility for anti-social behaviour. Instead of which anti-social behaviour often had no negative consequences for its perpetrators.

Another reason offered for the so-called 'youth problem' related to lack of community facilities and activities:

> There's not a lot for kids to do. They end up wandering the streets and some get involved in drugs and crime and drink – they are bored, walking the street, an easy target for drug-sellers.

So something has got to be done about that. (I28, FM)

Some older people don't mind us but some don't like it when there's a lot of us outside their houses. They always think we are up to something even when we are not – we just want to get out for a while, because we are stuck inside a lot. Nothing to do. People my age would like to have access to leisure centres where people could go swimming and things. (I31, FM, aged 17)

Interview participants referred to a growing range of stress-inducing pressures on young people. One of these was the pressure exerted by increasing levels of *consumerism*, which worked to create needs and desires for commodities that many working-class young people did not have access to:

Young people, because they are constantly told that our worth in society is our wealth, constantly made conscious of what they should have, what they should be wearing, what they should be eating, what car their parents should be driving, what they should be having for Christmas, what video games they should have – if they don't have these, there is stigma, and this leads to indifference. You can't avoid the pressures on TV all the time. Buy a new R-reg car. If you are constantly shown images of things which you are not able to fulfil, some youngsters aren't satisfied with what they have got. (I11, SM)

Even young children subjected one another to pressures to wear expensive clothes:

My grandson is 11 now at school, and the kids take the mickey out of him because his mum can't afford to buy him the trainers and the bomber jacket with all the labels on them. (I13, SM)

The array of commodities available to children, as well as television, had made young people more passive and less resourceful than they had been in the past:

When I was a child, life was dull, but we weren't bored. We would go on the road (no cars, no traffic) and spin tops, skip, keep ourselves busy. (I8, FW, 78)

Another pressure facing today's young people was that of *unemployment*:

In a way our parents had a harder life – because they didn't have the things that we had, like bicycles – but it was easier for them to get a job. There were lots of jobs in those days, it's much harder now. (I31, FM, aged 17)

One of the results of loosening constraints and increased stresses on young people was what people felt was a decrease in the age at which young people started to drink and smoke. Sixteen-year-old I12 felt that his age group had 'grown up' far more quickly than his mother's age group:

It's very different to when Mum was growing up. There's a lot more under-age drinking, life seems to be getting more dangerous, people are brought up in different ways – some parents care, others don't – so there'll be a lot more drinking and drugs and everything. Some of them can't handle it. People get into situations they don't have the experience to handle. (I12, FM, aged 16)

Furthermore people believed that illegal drugs were far more easily accessible as time passed and that increasingly younger people were getting involved in criminal activities, often to subsidise their drug intake:

Drugs were around even when I was at school, but nowadays they seem to force them on youngsters. A lot of kids experiment these days, like we all do in various ways, but the drugs they experiment with are just too strong for them, and they go out and do things like nick cars – youngsters do this. When I was a kid, it was people in their 30s who would nick cars, it all seems to be getting much younger and more violent. (I14, SM, 46 years)

When I was young there were no drugs, and you weren't allowed in pubs until you left school. And by the time you left school you had a job, so you could afford your pint. These days there are tremendous pressures on young people to take drugs and drink and they don't always have the money to do so. (I25, SM, 75 years)

The interviews supported the focus group finding that young people were considered far less of a problem in Sundon Park than in Farley. Farley people's response to the problem varied. For some, childish pranks were seen as criminal acts. They raged impotently about the problem, calling for the return of more aggressive policing, the reintroduction of corporal punishment and so on. I5 spoke of constantly being taunted by youngsters about his weight problem as he walked his two small daughters to school – a situation which distressed his children as much as it distressed him – and felt extremely undermined by the experience:

There is an element of kids that are ill disciplined and generally make life a nightmare for everyone else. (I5, FM)

Others attempted to be tolerant and understanding Some people feel that thefts and minor misdemeanours by children could be dealt with without police intervention being necessary, through approaching their parents in a concerned and positive way:

Last week someone saw some kids taking our washing and the missus chased them. The parents were OK. The Dad marched them up the stairs and they pulled it all out from under the bed – my t-shirts and things, and the father gave them a severe beating. No ways would I go to the police, not with childish things like that. Things like that can often be solved between neighbours if people are decent. If you approach kids in the right way . . . you don't have to make a mountain out of a molehill and be self-righteous about it. There are two ways of dealing with kids on your roof: 'Hey you fuckers, get off there or I'll beat you on the fucking arse', or 'Hey kids, come on down, you are going to fall and hurt yourselves'. In that way I don't kick them, they don't kick me and they climb down and go away. (I9, FM)

I always feel safe, because I know all the kids up here and if one of them took my car I would know who it was. They've grown up with my kids and I have got to know which ones are the thieves and which ones ain't. My son used to hang around with the neighbour's son and he would go there and the parents would never talk to him to find out who he was or what he was like. If his mum and dad knew some of the lads he has in there they would never let them through the door. You see, I know them, and they know me – and they know darn well that if someone took anything from my house I would know who it was. (I28, FM)

The position of women in the old days

We have already cited the warning by Pahl (1995) that romanticised views of past community life in England serve to conceal the fact that these idealised cohesive communities were often organised around socially exclusive and repressive hierarchies – characterised by, among other things, greater repression of women. Occasionally, interview participants expressed views that substantiated Pahl's claim. Buried in their positive accounts of the old days were comments which hinted at the existence of sexism, racism and discrimination against 'outsiders'.

I11 (SM), the only black informant in the in-depth interview sample, who spoke with feeling of the social exclusion and prejudice facing black people in contemporary Luton, commented that despite these problems, the situation had been worse when his grandmother had arrived in Luton from the Caribbean as a young woman:

Even now, people don't understand each other's cultures, and there seems little motivation to try and develop these understandings, but a lot of black people like my grandmother were considered as aliens when they first came across to the UK, but as time passes that is watering down, black people are becoming more and more acceptable here. A lot of things are getting more acceptable now. (I11, SM)

A number of informants spoke of the fact that the influx of non-Lutonians into the city in the 1950s was not welcomed by the 'old Lutonians'. Informants who had moved to Luton from other areas spoke of how difficult they had initially found it to integrate into the community, and how unwelcome 'outsiders' had been made to feel. I25 (SM) spoke of how he had suffered as a newcomer to Luton in the fifties when he had arrived there from Yorkshire to take up his job in the Vauxhall factory:

> I would never have picked Luton if I had known how it would be. In those days 'true Lutonians' hated everybody else that came to the town. People travelled in from all over to work at Vauxhall. In the fifties the Lutonians hated outsiders and they were mean with it. They would tell you 'It's time the council put up a road block and stopped you lot from coming in'. Luckily you have fewer and fewer of those old Lutonians now. (I25, SM)

I9 (FM) said he had suffered from what he had perceived as prejudice against the Scots when he had arrived in Luton fifteen years previously:

> The English here thought they were the number one. That they were superior to the rest of us – Scots, Irish, Welsh. That contributed very much to the low self-esteem that I suffered when I first came to Luton from Scotland. (I9, FM)

But more striking than references to prejudice against black people and outsiders were references by women to the fact that in many ways their lives were easier and more free of restricting social pressures than they had been in the past. They referred to the physical strain of housework in the old days where people had large families, and before the advent of household appliances. They referred to social and financial pressures on women to stay in bad marriages and to the extreme social stigma attached to pre-marital pregnancies. I16 spoke of being forced to stay in an unhappy marriage:

> There was nowhere for me to go [*when my marriage went wrong*]. People got married for life and just stuck it out purely because of the money side of it. If you had walked out and left you would have had no income and no home. A girl these days has social services behind her. She can pack her bags, walk out, and get backing. People get backing from their families these days. In those days one's parents would just say 'you have made your bed, now you must lie in it'. (I16, FW)

> You never admitted that you had marital problems. You sort of had to work it out for yourself. (I8, FW)

I7, whose own daughter had had a baby when she was 16, spoke of the shame and scandal that had ensued, comparing the relatively permissive attitudes of the present:

> When my daughter had a baby at 16, I was the scandal of the estate. It was considered a crime to have a child if you were unmarried. I myself had lived in terror of getting pregnant, I never had a man until my wedding night. People are more tolerant now. (I7, FW)

They also referred to the relative autonomy of wives compared to the old days:

> When I got married I used to love dancing but my husband put a stop to that. 'I don't like you going dancing, don't go,' he said. They wouldn't do that today, would they? (I7, FW)

In those days when you got married the husband kept up his interests and we, the wives, gave up ours and that was wrong. My husband kept up with his brass band and left me and the children at home on evenings and weekends for concerts. I was stuck at home with the children and not enough money to go anywhere myself. We never did things together. (I16, FW)

One informant, who had left her violent husband ten years previously after years of physical abuse and terror commented that the social support offered to battered women had improved considerably even in this ten-year period:

Nowadays it is much easier for battered women – much easier to get a court injunction and police protection than it was then. (I4, FW)

Conclusion

This chapter has considered three issues:
• to what extent does Putnam's concept of social capital resonate with ordinary people's experience of community life?
• which aspects of community life might serve as a source of health-enabling support or health-damaging strain?
• to what extent are there similarities and differences in forms and levels of social capital in our high-health ward and our low-health ward?

In relation to the first issue it must be emphasised that people's accounts of community life – both in the past and the present – were located almost exclusively in the interpersonal and informal spheres. As discussed in more detail in Chapter 5, references to any aspect of 'civic community' at the level of voluntary associations or civic networks of the type that Putnam speaks about were rare. Secondly it must be emphasised that there was no evidence of generalised community identity or trust (of the type that Putnam refers to) that extended beyond people's face-to-face circle of acquaintances. People said that while such identity and trust might have characterised community life in the past, the relative instability and mobility of contemporary working and living conditions, as well as the increasingly plural composition of communities, had undermined the possibility of such generalised levels of trust and identity existing in the present.

Levi (1996) and others cite Putnam's failure to provide a clear definition of trust as a shortcoming of his work. Implicit in the accounts of our informants was a clear conceptualisation of what they regarded as trust – a state where one could rely on others to act in one's best interests. Here best interests included: (i) having an attitude of general respect and tolerance, and more specifically (ii) respecting one's privacy and good reputation in the community – both through keeping confidences and avoiding spreading harmful gossip, and (iii) respecting one's physical safety and the safety of one's property.

Turning to the second concern of this chapter with regard to our interest in those aspects of community which served as a source of support or a source of strain, references to the past were most frequently used as a rhetorical device to pinpoint areas of stress in contemporary community life – in comparison to the positive relationships referred to in people's reconstructions of an idealised past. The two inter-connected issues leading to strain at the local community level were what people described as a range of community divisions which made it increasingly difficult for people to feel a sense of common social identity with other local residents – and closely linked to this low levels of trust (especially in relation to respect and tolerance between community members as well as respect for one another's physical safety and the safety of property). To a limited extent, lack of trust was articulated in relation to what people experienced as a growing sense of 'stranger danger' – mistrust of strangers – as well as a sense that levels of crime were on the increase. However the most powerful expressions of lack of trust related to the role of children and young people in the community. As in the focus groups, the problem of lack of trust was more pronounced in the relatively low-health district of Farley than in the relatively high-health area of Sundon Park.

In relation to a declining sense of local identity in an increasingly pluralistic society, informants from both communities referred to a range of divisions among local residents, along a range of fault-lines – relative affluence, age, ethnicity, residential status (home owners v. council tenants, tower block residents v. others). These fault-lines created clearly demarcated identity differences within particular wards, that increasingly undermined the sense of commonality that people said would be necessary to underpin the relationships of neighbourliness and reciprocal help and support which characterised their ideal concept of community.

These problems and divisions militated against a strong sense of unitary local identity of the kind that Putnam refers to in his definition of social capital. However, there was an interesting tension in people's accounts of community – which the past–present comparisons highlighted. On the one hand people referred to a 'breakdown in community' – because community life was not characterised by the community-wide and all-inclusive levels of trust and identity that they believed to have prevailed in the past. On the other hand, their references to community breakdown were punctuated by their accounts of strong networks of supportive relationships – based on the very trust, identity and reciprocity which they said was lacking in their particular ward of relevance. This point is taken up in Chapter 5 which examines the three types of social networks referred to by interview participants, and concludes that the types of networks that played a key role in people's lives were often either narrower or (particularly in the case of our high-health ward) wider than the place-based local community dimension that Putnam highlights in his definition of social capital. We will argue that rather than 'breaking down' as informants implied, community life has transformed or evolved in response to changing social conditions which have led to a changing and more varied set of social needs among community members. These changes have taken place in such a way that Putnam's notion of community cohesion bears a closer resemblance to people's romanticised accounts of an idealised past than to their experiences of the contemporary present. We will argue that this notion needs to be extensively reworked if it is to be used as a tool for understanding contemporary local community life in England.

5. Civic engagement 1: Informal networks of friends and neighbours

Chapters 5, 6 and 7 examine the main networks and associations available to residents of Farley and Sundon Park; the types of support and assistance they offer; and factors which promote or hinder access to them. Finally consideration will be given to the extent to which each of these networks and associations contribute to positive levels of community cohesion, which Putnam (1993a) regards as the key component of social capital.

According to Putnam, the positive community relationships (trust, reciprocity, civic identity) constituting social capital are associated with dense horizontal networks of voluntary community organisations and associations, interlocking with state-provided services and facilities. In Putnam's work such voluntary associations include choral societies, bird-watching clubs, soccer clubs, Lions Clubs and so on. It is involvement in these organisations that leads to the high levels of trust, reciprocity and positive community identity which Putnam argues are the root of good local government.

In the interests of exploring the extent to which Putnam's conceptualisation of social capital is appropriate for understanding local communities in England, we examine informants' accounts of their significant social networks. Three types of networks featured in the in-depth interviews: *informal face-to-face networks of relatives, neighbours and friends* (for example old school friends, former neighbours, friends met on holiday, current or former work associates) (discussed in this chapter); *voluntary associations linked to leisure, hobbies and personal development* (for example snooker, Scouts, mother and toddler groups, churches) (see Chapter 6); and *formal and informal community activist networks and initiatives* (tenants' or residents' associations, Neighbourhood

Watch groups) (see Chapter 7). We will argue that involvement in the more organised voluntary associations and community networks of the type that Putnam refers to (the second and third network types referred to above) was not a widespread feature of life in either of our wards of interest. People's significant social networks tended to consist of the first group of networks, that is informal networks of friends and relatives.

Furthermore, consistent with our hypothesis that levels of social capital are higher in Sundon Park than Farley, there was evidence that Sundon Park residents drew on a wider range of networks than their Farley counterparts – both locally within the ward, and outside of the ward. While Farley people's lives tended to be more locally based, Sundon Park residents' networks also crossed the relatively confined boundaries of the geographical ward, with people being involved in a range of activities (work, leisure, family-related, religious and so on) which took place outside of the boundaries of Sundon Park.

The remainder of this chapter has four parts, focusing in turn on;
- what emerged as people's most significant social networks, that is informal networks of relatives, neighbours and friends, and the types of support they offered;
- the marked gender differences in the way in which these networks are created, accessed and sustained by women and by men;
- factors enhancing the development of these informal networks; and
- factors hindering the development and quality of these networks.

The greatest obstacle to the development of such informal networks seemed to exist in the high-rise tower blocks at the edge of one of our wards of interest. Information regarding gender differences in informal networking, as well as the limitations on networking in the tower blocks compared to other housing forms, leads us to argue that there are often strong within-community differences in the distribution and availability of social capital.

1. Friends, neighbours and relatives

People referred to relatives, neighbours and friends as their key support and friendship networks. Those people whose families were alive and accessible always turned to them as first source of support, particularly in relation to financial difficulties. *Financial problems* were often regarded as a major source of embarrassment, with people trying to solve these within their immediate families or through the help of bank loans or debt counselling, but often trying to conceal such problems from friends and neighbours for as long as possible. People varied in their attitudes to seeking *emotional support*. In the interviews emotional support took two forms – pleasant companionship and sociability on the one hand and support in times of sadness or stress on the other. With regard to the latter, people again almost invariably turned to their families first where they were accessible. With regard to confiding in friends and neighbours, some tended to be particularly secretive about marital problems. Problems relating to death, illness or children were regarded as less embarrassing, and here people seemed more comfortable in soliciting emotional support from friends and neighbours as well as relatives. In relation to pleasant companionship people sought out friends, neighbours and relatives interchangeably. With regard to *practical problems* (for example assistance with car repairs, borrowing tools, moving furniture or house-watching and pet-feeding in one's absence) neighbours were generally the first line of call. Neighbours were also generally the first line of call in *emergencies* such as fires, accidents, or sudden illness.

Other examples of help and support between neighbours included actions such as buying sweets for neighbours' children, cooking for husbands and children if wives were in hospital, first aid with home accidents, contributing to the layette of neighbours' pregnant teenage daughters, keeping a set of spare keys in the event of people being locked out of their homes, exchanging food (especially with Asian neighbours), listening to problems, giving personal advice, sharing holiday photographs, baby-sitting and taking in parcels. Here it must be emphasised that there were great individual differences in the types of help and support people gave and received from neighbours. People were mixed in the extent to which they drew on neighbours for help with child care, for example, as these two responses from Sundon Park women suggest:

> We always look after each other's kids if one of us is going to the doctor or the dentist and if I am out and late, I can always phone a neighbour to ask her to collect the kids for me. There is always the back-up of that. (I27, SW)

> I would be reluctant to ask people to look after the children, because you feel you have got to help them back – and it's not always easy to have them back. I would rather take my children with me to the doctor, and put up with them, than asking for help. Also if you take a child to a friend's place you talk for 20 minutes when you drop them off and 20 minutes when you come back, that adds up to 40 extra minutes when there is so much else to be done. (I6, SW)

In this report we will not deal with family networks (Putnam defines social capital specifically in terms of extra-family networks) other than to say that those who had access to their families generally referred to them as their major support networks:

> Most things are dealt with in the immediate family, but there is always the back-up of the neighbours there. We haven't needed to call on them for major things, but they are there if needed. (I22, FW)

After the family, the informal friendship networks we discuss here formed people's second most importance sources of support (if not their most important sources where families were not available). These networks had two defining characteristics. Their first feature was their micro-locality, generally existing among people who lived in the same close or street, or else within walking distance of one another's homes – in contrast to the networks of which Putnam speaks, which tend to cover more widespread community localities. Secondly they tended to be confined to people who were personally acquainted with one another, in contrast to Putnam's more generalised notion of trust – which extended to people one was not acquainted with. As has already been discussed, informants in both our wards said that one should be wary of trusting people one did not know.

In this chapter we look at three different patterns of creating, sustaining and accessing informal networks – associated with women, married men and single men with responsibilities. We speculate that a fourth and fifth group would be teenagers and young single people without children. Little information emerged on social networking among these groups save for one comment by I14, who had recently moved in with his partner and a new baby. He compared the community commitment of single people and family members:

> Families make a community more than single people. There's more responsibilities, you are more geared to looking after other people. When I was single I mostly thought about enjoying myself. As my child [*now aged one*] grows up I will be more interested in the community – once I need to find out about schools, safety aspects . . . (I14, SM)

Information about such differences will contribute to our claim that if Putnam's notion of social capital is to be used as a tool for understanding local communities in England, it needs to be reworked in a way that emphasises that this community resource is not equally available to all community members in any kind of homogeneous way.

2. Gendered nature of informal networks

As we have already said, most people regarded their spouses, parents and other close relatives as their primary source of emotional support. In addition to this, *women* also generally gave and received a great deal of support from strong face-to-face *local* networks of personal acquaintances, mostly with other women. These friendships were often based on the sharing of experiences relating to relationships and child care. Where necessary, *married men* tended to access these local neighbourhood networks through their wives, but they did not seem to draw on them very heavily. When they did draw on them it was often to do with practical problems relating to car or home maintenance. Those friends that they did have were often linked to work or *non-local* social and sports clubs – and these friendships tended on the whole to be less intimate than their wives' friendships. The men that did draw directly on these otherwise women-generated local neighbourhood networks tended to be men with sick spouses, or divorced or widowed men – who needed support either with child care, or else because of their own health problems or old age. Each of these patterns is discussed in turn.

There was general acknowledgement that it was women who created local community:

> The nucleus of community starts when wives and mothers are at home. They talk to each other, and it spreads. (I29, FM)

> It's the wife who knows all the neighbours. I would say hallo to them all, but for the life of me, I don't know their names or anything. I do say Good Morning, or Good Evening, but I have never been on social terms with any of them. (I25, SM)

> My wife is more outgoing and knows all the people in the road, which I don't. (I36, SM)

> When people know that someone in the community is sick, they always go around visiting. My wife will say 'I must go and see so and so, she's ill in bed' and away she goes. Just to ask if the person needs anything. You do get men doing this but not so often. I mean once you have been to see them it's a long time before a man goes back again. (I25, SM)

People repeatedly referred to gender differences in community networking in a range of contexts. One of these was in response to questions about informants' own parents' social and associational lives. Again and again they spoke of their mothers as the family's major social networker when they were growing up:

> Mum talked to the neighbours, she's chatty, but dad, he's always been very much to himself. (I27, SW)

> Father just worked, and joined in anything that mother organised. (I3, SW)

> Mum did more linking with neighbours than Dad – he didn't have anything against it, but he is very quiet really and goes with the flow. Mum takes the initiative socially. (I6, SW)

This theme persisted into people's accounts of community life in the present:

> Women try harder to connect with others in the community, they make more of an active effort to keep in touch – through birthday cards and . . . my husband would never send a birthday card. (I6, SW)

My son and my husband are either at home or at work. Neither of them do anything sociable. (I3, SW)

Men don't talk to anybody. Women show their emotions, they talk about them if they have a problem . . . if half the husbands knew how we talk up at the school gates about their illnesses, their sex lives, they would die of embarrassment. A group of girls get together and have a right dig at the blokes and those body bits that substitute for their brains. Men don't get support apart from their wives. My husband would never sit and talk like this [*i.e. the interview*]. I don't even know sometimes that there's anything wrong with him, I wish I could get inside his head sometimes. They do their best to sort things out on their own. When I was pregnant I didn't know he was being made redundant – men don't know how to seek support, and they sort of press on without it. (I27, SW)

Women are much more involved in local things, knowing people, supporting them. I can go to the shops and be talking and my husband doesn't know a soul. He works staggered shifts in London and when he has time he goes to the pub. So he's never around before 8 pm. (I27, SW)

If a boy is hurt or worried about something he will usually just make a joke of it. Girls, they think it's easier to talk. They think, 'Oh no, they won't think badly of me if I tell this or that'. Boys, they think, 'If I tell him he will tell everyone and they will take the mick and say things about me'. (I31, SM)

Several people said the quality of women's friendships was more sustaining than men's friendships. Women spoke of sharing confidences, offering one another support. Men spoke more of telling jokes and discussing sport:

[*What do you talk about with your friends at the club?*] We all speak, have laughs, tell jokes, take the mickey. (I35, SM)

It was often through their role as primary child carers that women created community:

It's really through children that you get to know one another. It's children who help you get involved in the community, because when you go down to the school you see other people and get talking and that's how you build friendships. (I6, SW)

One really good thing about Sundon Park is that mothers can walk their children to school, and have a chance to get to know each other, to natter on the street and at the school gate. (I10, SW)

I chat with the other mothers at school. We have a laugh, and moan about the husband and moan about the kids . . . it helped. We'll giggle, say to one another 'You look haggard today, had a bad morning?' (I34, SW)

Who do I see? I take the kids swimming and see mums at swimming. I take the kids to football and see mums at football. (I34, SW)

Older women whose own children had left home spoke of creating 'surrogate' family relationships with neighbours' children. For example, I8 said that the affection that she felt for the children in the community gave her a sense of rootedness in Farley:

> With no grandchildren of my own, I have adopted my neighbour's son as my grandson. (I8, FW)

Even I7, who had many complaints about her neighbour's unruly children, felt some affiliation with them:

> My neighbour's children do look on me as some sort of grandmother figure. Even though they are a nuisance most of the time, I still like them. (I7, FW)

In the light of the demands and isolation of full-time child care, single mothers in our sample laid particular emphasis on the importance of informal support networks:

> If you are alone you rely very much on your friends and on your family . . . single mums also have to rely on each other much more than most people. I know a lot of mums in the benefit queue, because I know many on income support and a lot do go down there on a Monday. (I4, FW)

In comparison with women who often reached outside the family for help, men relied primarily on close family for support.

> Neighbours can help with small things, like gardening or your car. But people tend to deal with big problems within the close family. (I31, FM)

> In my life I have dealt with problems on my own, or with my family. I don't look to people outside the family for help. (I5, FM)

Men tended to suffer in silence if family support was not available. Thus, for example, I5 (FM) said he visited his mother in London when his relationship with his wife was particularly stressful – or else resorted to confiding in strangers in pubs or barmaids.

In relation to local networks of friends or neighbours, men tended not to participate in these at all, or else accessed them through their wives. Unless they had a particular crisis (in which case they leaned on neighbours very heavily), men tended to stress their social independence:

> I look after myself. I don't ask a great many other people for anything. (I11, SM)

> I haven't talked about my wife's death at all. I don't know why – my daughter has been for bereavement counselling. I keep it to myself, but I'm all right. I often go to bed and think about

it and have a little cry, and that's all. In fact this interview is the first time I have talked about it since she died [*a year previously*] (I25, SM)

My husband is not one to talk to people. I believe in talking to people for support when things are bad. (I27, SW)

The group of men that did tend to reach out to informal community networks, particularly for practical help, were men who were single (widowed or divorced), especially if they were ill or had children. I28 (FM), a divorced single father of three children, relied heavily on his friend's wife for support:

My wife left me with three schoolchildren, one is mentally disabled. I had to be mum, dad, nurse, provider, chief cook and bottle washer. I get a lot of help from my mate's wife, K's mum, they live up the street. She has helped me a hell of a lot. (I28, FM)

He also relied on his nephews, who lived close by, to take his learning disabled son to the community centre on one or two evenings a week to give him some respite from his caring role. I26 referred to the 'magnificent support' he had got from local people throughout his wife's illness and then death from cancer:

When my wife was ill, bloody hell, they couldn't do enough for me, my friends and neighbours. I could never leave her on her own. They were very helpful, going shopping for me, sitting with her. And the district nurse came in every day, the doctor gave me his home number and would often come during the night, my boss was very helpful giving me time off, the neighbours were in and out doing our shopping, I shall be ever grateful to them, a lovely crowd. (I26, SM)

For the funeral, my gang are all from Ireland, and the neighbours put them all up – because there's nothing here, hotels, or baby-sitters, or B and Bs. (I26, SM)

I13 (SM), a widower, derived much of his social contact from working in his garage workshop that opened on to the close, where neighbours would stop as they passed by, mostly to chat, but sometimes to offer to bring him small items from the local shops.

I32, a 78-year-old widower, had developed a close and sustaining relationship with his 42-year-old neighbour – a divorced woman whose husband had left her with a disabled child and no support:

I taught my neighbour to drive and helped her to get a cheap second-hand car to transport the child. She said 'Oh P, you are like a father to me'. She comes in for a cup of tea in the morning, to tell me her troubles – I also got her to go to college to do an —— course. There was a bloke up the road who had lost his mum. I persuaded her to go and knock on his door one day and offer help when he had the flu, and now they are going together. She is much happier now. (I32, FM)

3. Factors enhancing the quality of informal networks

Chapter 2 has already discussed how factors relating to trust and local identity serve to help or hinder the development of reciprocal help and support and of neighbourliness in our wards of interest. In this chapter we focus on four additional factors which informants said served to enhance the quality of informal networks: the planning or layout of streets and closes; the length of residence of community members; common ethnicity; and the existence of overlapping group memberships.

Planning: There was general agreement that closes and small streets were the best setting for the development of neighbourliness. Those who lived on busy roads tended to spend less time outside and thus have less contact with neighbours:

> It's wonderful here, we have a clover leaf of cul-de-sacs, it's clean, quiet, you get to know everyone. (I21, FW)

> When I go out I often run into people I haven't seen, and we stop and have a little natter. (I8, FW)

Length of residence: Many interview participants referred to length of residence as a key factor in shaping close local networks:

> I just love it here, I have always lived up here, so I am used to it . . . I'm well known because I've lived here so long, I know everyone and they know me. (I7, FW)

> A lot of the estate was built in the 50s and 60s and a lot of people moved in at the same time. Things weren't great then, nearly everyone was struggling – and we all got to know each other well. These days there is a strong feeling of a sense of belonging – that we all came at the same time. While there have been a lot of changes, a lot of people have stayed. This makes for neighbourliness. (I36, SM)

> When I was younger I knew everyone – now I'm older the only friends I have are those who have been here as long as we have – and they are dwindling now, through death or through moving away. (I16, FW)

Common ethnicity: People frequently referred positively, even enviously, to the way in which ethnicity tended to bind sub-groups within the community. Several people referred to the strong links within the Irish community, which cut across particular local community boundaries or neighbourhoods:

My wife is Irish. The Irish have much more of a sense of community in so many ways. There are pubs one can go to where they are all Irish people. It doesn't matter what part of Ireland you come from, they come together and are like a family. They still maintain an awful lot of their culture. If the club has music it will be Irish-type musicians. Irish sports on TV etc. (I5, FM)

There is a close bond between the Irish around here. It comes naturally the Irish thing, we all know each other. (I36, SM)

The Irish community here is large, we all know each other. (I25, SM)

Not all Irish people chose to capitalise on this 'identity resource' however:

Being Irish is not a big part of my life here. Rather than seeing myself as Irish I see myself as a person, concerned with living my life and paying my way. (I26, FM)

While such identities were generally referred to in a positive way, some informants hinted at their exclusivity:

There is a large Irish population here too – in pubs you don't admit to being English – and you hear a fair bit of racial claptrap, and anti-English remarks which I find strange because I think 'If you hate us that much why do you live here?' (I5, FM)

Overlapping group memberships: Another factor generating community was overlapping group memberships – the more one's networks overlapped, the more likely one was to make contact with people:

At church we end up talking to parents of kids the kids are at school with. At the kids' school there is a man who works with me on the trains, so often I will talk to him while we are waiting. (I5, FM)

4. Factors hindering the quality of small-scale informal neighbourhood networks

In the interviews, informants mentioned a range of obstacles to the development of robust informal neighbourhood networks. These included: conflicts over issues such as noise or the use of communal space; the 'emptying out' of the community during the day as more and more people, including women (traditionally the main props of local community) worked increasingly far from home; the phenomenon of 'stranger danger'; the fear of being taken advantage of by neighbours; the competing demands of family and work demands which left little time for community; and obstacles to community in the tower blocks.

Conflicts: These often arose even between the most well-meaning of neighbours. Often people's goodwill was sorely tested, and informants stressed that lack of tolerance was often the root of much strain and bitterness. Chapter 4 referred to I9's (FM) policy of approaching the parents of children who had stolen his washing rather than involving the police. People often emphasised the importance of approaching people personally at first, rather than calling in the police or lawyers as some community members did:

> When we have had the odd disco or someone playing music very loud I have trotted around and sweetly asked them to turn it down, and they have done it. (I40, SW)

I6 (SW) spoke of an extremely unpleasant situation that had developed in her street, where one neighbour had sent a lawyer's letter to another about problems relating to parking in a shared driveway. The second neighbour had been incensed and insulted that the first neighbour had chosen to bring in a lawyer rather than attempting to resolve the matter privately. A second lawyer had been brought in and the situation was escalating out of all proportion – spoiling the atmosphere in what had previously been a congenial street-based network.

She said that she and her husband had learned the importance of consideration and tolerance from a problem that developed with their former neighbours:

> The last neighbours – our houses were really close together, and we had some music on too early in the morning when they were sleeping. I said sorry, but my apology was not accepted, and she got a bit nasty after that. We have learned lessons from that. You have to be tolerant of each other if you don't like some things, or things can escalate and become unpleasant for everyone. If you say something you will probably upset someone, it's sometimes better to tolerate than to comment. (I6, SW)

The focus groups have already highlighted the problem of children, balls and gardens, and in-depth interview participants did the same:

> The kids play football up here because there's a bit of space in the close, and they use our neighbour's hedge as a goal. She's constantly driven mad by the ball hitting her door because she thinks someone is knocking. When she goes to the door and finds one of these oicks picking up his ball and asks him to be careful, I have heard them say 'O shut up, you silly fat cow', or some mouthful of abuse. (I5, FM)

While this problem was clearly a source of stress to several adults in our sample, particularly older people who took great pride in their gardens, I7 (FW) emphasised the lengths she had gone to avoid this sort of strain, pulling up her much loved flower beds and replacing them with lawn after new neighbours moved in with unruly children:

> I make myself get on with the neighbours, because you've got to live here, and I like to live in peace and harmony, so a lot of things I overlook. I used to have a lovely front garden with a bed full of beautiful flowers when we were just old people living up here, but with the young women who moved into the street they let the children run all over my garden and trample on everything and kill it. So I dug everything up and put lawn down. I thought, well, there's no good making myself ill, keep looking at the children ruining my garden. And I feel better in myself, because I had felt the stress of it all. (I7, FW)

Community deserted during the day: Another factor that hindered the development of local community spirit, particularly in Sundon Park, was the fact that parts of the community were deserted during the day, with more and more women going out to work, and people working increasingly greater distances from their homes:

> Everybody along this road is out at work during the day. When I was on shift work I would have the street to myself. You never saw anyone, it was like the grave. (I35, SM)

Young people in Farley had created a thriving youth culture – where groups of young people would meet in the streets, outside the local shops or in a range of local open spaces. By contrast, no such community existed among young people in Sundon Park:

> The only time I see my friends is if I phone them. Nobody comes out otherwise. We might meet in someone's house, have a chat, watch some TV. Or we phone, see what is going on, then usually get into someone's car and go off. There's nothing going on here. (I38, SM, 17 years)

'*Stranger danger*': Earlier chapters have already referred to informants' perceptions that one should not trust people unless one had known them for a fairly long time. This perception often stood in the way of people giving or receiving help from neighbours.

> I've had good help and support from close friends – but I would never think of turning to rely on any old Fred Bloggs just because he lived across the road. (I34, SW)

A range of 'dangers' could potentially result from unwary sociability or offers of assistance to people that one had not known for long. Farley people tended to emphasise the 'safety of property' element of trust in explaining why one should be wary of all community members except for those one knew well:

> People are scared to help others because they think they are going to get ripped off. If they help someone they will take something off them and then don't want to know – that's part of life nowadays. (I9, FM)

> You have to be a bit wary these days. That's the way things are now. You invite someone into your home, you don't know whether they are looking your house over to see if they can burgle it. Basically, well, no one knows anyone else these days. (I28, FM)

Sundon Park people tended to emphasise the 'danger of gossip' aspect of trust, as well as norms regarding social boundary maintenance, privacy and 'not interfering' – already cited at length by Sundon Park participants in the focus groups:

> Society has changed. I see the local children playing in the street, if it starts raining hard I would be reluctant to ask them in as I would have twenty years ago. People have such funny ideas – they might think I was being a busybody, or ask why I didn't send them back to their own homes. You get to a point where you think: 'well I'll just ignore them', which isn't in my make-up. (I10, SW)

> I don't believe in sharing one's problems with people beyond very close friends and family – firstly because I don't trust people in general, and secondly because I don't like people to interfere in my business. (I34, SW)

Unintended consequences of friendly gestures: People referred to a range of potentially unintended consequences arising from friendly gestures. One was being 'stuck' with uncongenial friends that one could not get rid of:

> One should be wary of everyone at first, and not get friendly too quickly. If you do get friendly with some people you can't get rid of them. It's too late if you find there are things about them you don't like. (I17, SW)

Another was the fact that offering emotional support to neighbours could become exhausting and burdensome:

> My one neighbour comes and tells me her worries. She's a good soul, but sometimes when I see her coming I think 'Oh dear, what is she going to tell me this time'. She gets very depressed and I feel I have to listen to her. My head is spinning by the time she has gone, sometimes after two hours. (I10, SW)

> Every night our neighbour, a widower who was bed-ridden, would give me a ring, and I would have to sit with him for a couple of hours. I didn't mind doing it, but it got a bit much when I said 'I have to go to the club' at 8 pm one Friday, and he said 'Stay here with me rather'. I thought 'Hell this is getting tedious, he'll have me in here 24 hours a day'. (I25, SM)

Several people feared that those who offered help to others too generously opened themselves up to the risk of being taken advantage of:

C [*a single mother across the road who often helps friends with child care*] gets used and dumped – you have to be careful that people don't take advantage of you. I don't let myself get used. I mean I will sometimes look after friends' children, but if I don't feel like it I will say, 'No – I'm sorry but I don't want to'. (I4, FW)

Competing priorities: Several people often said that much as they might want to be neighbourly in principle, they simply didn't have time:

If a person is in trouble you might really want to help them, but sometimes there's only so much you can do – you are constrained by how much you have to work and by your duties to your family. You can't talk forever to a depressed neighbour – because the meal won't get cooked, and the homework won't get done – it simply wouldn't be fair to the rest of the family. (I6, SW)

Most people look out for their own interests. As it has become harder for people to make a living, and the amount of time they need to put into it leaves less and less time for other things, you are forced to be inward looking, especially if you have a young family. (I29, FM)

Obstacles to community in tower blocks: The greatest obstacle to the development of the informal networks of friends and neighbours referred to by interview participants was referred to by the two informants who lived in the Marsh Farm tower blocks in Sundon Park. While the perceptions of two people will clearly need to be backed up with further research drawing on a larger sample, these two men (one single in his 30s, and one in his 40s who lived with his partner and baby) pointed to a range of obstacles to the development of neighbourliness in these huge, ugly and impersonal living spaces. They highlighted the way in which the social stigmatisation of the area (exacerbated by sensationalistic and inaccurate media reporting of the Marsh Farm riots) had undermined the flat-dwellers' sense of esteem and made a positive community identity almost impossible to sustain.

Both regretted the lack of communal spaces, and the impersonal anonymity of residents. Such factors, combined with the rapid turnover of neighbours, led to a lack of caring and interest in one another's affairs:

I know what my neighbour looks like and I might see him, and say 'All right' and that's it. It's not a close-knit block. People here don't speak. I have not been in anyone's flat. I have been here three years and perhaps see people in the passageway or lift. My neighbour, there seems nothing wrong with him. He seems a nice enough geezer, but I don't envisage that he will be around here for long. It just seems so temporary that we don't bother. Our contact will last as long as it takes for the lift to come up or go down and that's it. (I11, SM)

Help my neighbours? I don't have any relationship with my neighbours. I can't see any basis that would arise for helping each other. That's just accepted here. Everyone just keeps himself to himself. I don't think people should get involved. I hear domestic arguments, I hear people screaming, I don't run and find out what is going on. (I11, SM)

> There are more people above you, more people below you, but very few on the same level. Because you don't know people to talk to, invite in for a chat or whatever I don't think you worry too much if something happens to someone – it's not that you are nasty, but you probably wouldn't give it a second thought because you don't know them. (I14, SM)

I14 worried about his child growing up in a context without community networks:

> There's no communal areas here, no place or reason to interact with anyone. I don't think you can have community in a tower block. It's not like if you live in a row of houses and you have got the back garden and the front garden and relationships could develop from there. I worry about my child growing up in these flats, he won't have as many friends to play with from the immediate area as I had growing up in a house in a street. Here we are very isolated. (I14, SM)

He spoke of the stresses of living in a place where there was simultaneously a lack of privacy, but in a completely anonymous context:

> I think a lot of problems would be solved if they got rid of these tower blocks. They breed a lot of trouble – noise for one thing, no real privacy. You can hear the least noise from the other flats and when it's continuous you are never really at ease. One's a tiny bit stressed all the time, you can never relax totally. (I14, SM)

I11 spoke of the social stigma attached to the flats:

> I do see my aunts, they live around the corner and I visit them more than they visit me. I think people have certain stigmas about visiting the flats. Some people just don't feel comfortable coming here. They all live in semi-detached houses, houses with gardens. (I11, SM)

> People are a bit ashamed of Sundon Park after the Marsh Farm riots – it was right-wing people from elsewhere causing all the trouble, and rent-a-mobs brought in. But it was reported as if it was local people. (I3, SW)

5. Concluding comment

This chapter has provided an account of informal networks, which informants cited as their most important source of social capital. Three features distinguish these informal networks from Putnam's criteria for social capital. *Firstly* these networks tended to exist at the micro-level, generally of the street or the close, rather than the level of the geographical community. *Secondly* they tended to be exclusive and small-scale, usually only extending to a small group of people well known to one another. Their exclusivity was based on the belief that one should be wary of people one didn't know, a wariness of getting 'stuck' with friends one had made too quickly, and a desire for privacy and a 'non-interfering' environment (especially among people in Sundon Park). *Thirdly* there were marked gender differences in the way in which these networks were accessed by women and men. This report highlights Putnam's neglect of such small-scale, often geographically micro-level, informal networks of friends, neighbours and relatives, which our data suggest are the major source of social capital available to members of local English communities.

6. Civic engagement 2: Voluntary networks linked to leisure, hobbies and personal development

In this chapter we examine the second network type referred to in our interviews, and the extent to which such voluntary organisations were a feature of the social lives of our informants. We provide case studies of the two groups in this network category that were mentioned most frequently by our informants, that is the church and the Scouts. In the light of the minimal role played by such groupings in the lives of our informants, the chapter concludes with an account of some of the factors that hindered involvement in such groupings.

1. Associations linked to leisure, hobbies and personal development

Putnam associates social capital with voluntary community organisations and associations – such as choral societies and bird-watching clubs. High levels of participation in dense horizontal networks of such groupings, interlocking with state-provided services and facilities, allegedly lead to the high levels of trust, reciprocity and positive community identity which are the essential feature of cohesive local communities.

Equivalent groupings referred to in our interviews were categorised as *voluntary associations linked to leisure, hobbies and personal development*. Involvement in the more organised voluntary associations of this type was not a widespread feature of life in our wards of interest. Groups referred to in our in-depth interviews included pubs, clubs, snooker, dominoes, sports groupings, referred to by men only; Cubs/Brownies/Scouts and mother and toddler groups referred to by women only; and church and church-related groupings, youth clubs, bingo and pensioners' groupings mentioned by both genders. However references to such organisations tended to be isolated and made in passing. Furthermore, apart from a pensioners' club, bingo and the youth club, which were held in the council-run Farley community centre, none of these activities had the interlocking relationships with local government or state-related organisations – and, as we shall see, people tended to have a passive client–provider relationship with the community centre and its activities. Only one informant (I35) was involved in any voluntary charity-type work, working as a part-time carer with a Catholic group, and making breakfast at a centre for the homeless every morning (with both of these activities outside of Sundon Park where he lived). He spoke of the positive role this work played in his life:

> I have always done volunteer work, because of my religion – I suppose my conscience is easier if I do, and strangely, doing these things, one gets a lot out of it. It's hard to define what – it makes me feel better. It keeps me going, gets me out and about. It does you good, a man comes into the [*homeless*] centre and he's down in the dumps, and you say 'Hallo George', and even to hear his name mentioned by someone else gives him a lift. (I35, SM)

The voluntary group that was discussed in the most detail was the church (and church-related groups and activities), and a few older women referred to having been involved in local Scouts/Cubs groupings in the past. Each of these groupings will be discussed briefly before turning to examine factors which encouraged or hindered people's involvement in such groups.

2. Case studies of two voluntary groupings

The church

I6 referred to the ambiguity of the church in relation to the community. On the one hand it had the infrastructure and personnel to play a key role in community-building. On the other hand, in an increasingly secular society, its appeal was very limited:

The church has so much infrastructure, buildings in each area, networks, and ministers are the closest we have to community leaders really, and in one way this role could be built up much further. But the church says so many things that make people uncomfortable. It just puts so many people off. (I6, SW)

While the church didn't appeal to the majority of citizens, it did provide a crucial source of support and community for those who were members. Those who were involved in the church made many references to its positive role as a community-enhancing social network:

I think so many people need the church. There's an awful lot of people out there who are hurting and who are ill. Especially if they don't have families to go to, or they feel they can't go to their families. That is what the church is there for. It's a bit like family if you like, aunties, uncles, someone who can help you and be there for you. (I40)

Even some of those who were opposed to the church recognised this (with I29 commenting that the church played a similarly positive networking function to the laundromat):

If you go to church that is a good way of meeting people – I don't go to church any more – I quite enjoy the benefits and the rules, if you like, which applied properly are excellent, but I don't like men dressing up in frocks and it's another way of keeping people subjugated anyhow, but in churches you meet people – therefore you get to know people and talk. They are a catalyst for promoting friendships. If people talk . . . it's like most people around here who haven't got a washing machine know more people than those that do from going to the laundromat. (I29, FM)

Churchgoers spoke at length about the role which church members played in a range of contexts. It provided support through marital crises – support which some informants felt was more effective than neighbourhood support networks:

We have a busy social life with about fifteen other [Jehovah's] Witness families – drawn from all over Luton. We spend a lot of time visiting in other areas. We find we tend to have more in common with people from our church than with people from our immediate neighbourhood; I wouldn't go out of my way to make friends outside of our Witness circle. We trust each other, share beliefs and values – morality, honesty, trustworthiness – love basically. (I22, FW)

I think I can talk more to people at church than to the neighbours, especially when I was going through the divorce with my first husband . . . people just seemed more understanding there, than going around to a neighbour's house. (I30, FW)

Churches also provide informed counselling to those in debt, visiting church members in prison, supporting young mothers and the elderly and so on. I40 spoke of her twice-weekly morning work in the church with great enthusiasm, and emphasised the inclusiveness of these events:

> We bring in half the congregation to lay out tea, sandwiches for mothers and toddlers, and then to clear up afterwards – the kids have a riotous time – it's a nice thing to do for people who haven't got anyone, to know there is a luncheon laid on. It's nice – every member of the community can come and feel welcome, so you don't have to be at home and lonely all the time. This is what the church premises should be for – to be thrown open for people to have fun and support each other. (I40, SW)

It also played a role in establishing contacts with people from other congregations in a wide range of areas.

Despite the advantages referred to by those few informants who were church members, the church lacked relevance and interest to the majority of our sample. The main reason cited for declining church attendance was its lack of relevance to modern life:

> A lot of people my gran's age go to church – it has always meant a lot to them. But as generations go on, it means less and less. There is a lot of social pressures on us these days that have nothing to do with church and church values. My grandmother was a devout churchgoer, but those kind of values are getting more and more watered out, as the generations go on the church moves less and less. A lot of social pressures that we face have nothing to do with church or church values. (I11, SM)

> I would do more for my church, it's important to me, but my husband is not interested, he is frightened of religion, it's just not relevant to him. (I6, SW)

Both I6 and I3 referred to the growing gap between the needs of the parishioners and the availability of facilities as churches had to become increasingly geared towards raising money:

> There are so many young mums at home on their own, without much money – people are struggling to pay off their mortgages – but they could afford to get around there for 25p on a Tuesday morning for a chat with other mums, where the children could play together. The new vicar said we couldn't have the hall any more – he rented it out to a chap running a dancing school who could pay more money. I had been paying the vicar rent for using the building, but it didn't cover the cost of the heating. The C of E should have managed its money better. (I3, SW)

The same vicar had incurred the irritation of a number of church members through his top-down leadership style. He had closed down the Mothers' Union group, and driven away the Scout group from service attendance:

> He said he closed it down because there were only a few members – but we think it irritated him having an outside organisation in the church. (I3, SW)

> The new vicar also alienated the Scout group – we used to take about 30 Scouts there for services, and the church is very cold, so we used to let them chat while they were waiting for the service to start, how can one keep 30 cold kids quiet. He couldn't accept this so we stopped taking the Scouts there. The two previous vicars had really done their best to encourage youngsters. (I3, SW)

In both wards, people tended to belong to churches that were physically located outside the area.

The Scouts

Scouts and Guides groupings appeared to have served as successful community-building exercises up until the recent past, generating jumble sales, sponsored walks, collective activities such as painting the Scout hut, knitting dolls' clothes and so on. As I10 said, 'With the Scouts we were always busy, busy, busy.' Women spoke of the great satisfaction they had derived from this work, despite the time and energy that it took:

> We were very involved in the Scouts and Brownies – very much a community. [*What did you gain from this involvement?*] Satisfaction. At the end of the day of a jumble sale, you had been there from 9 in the morning to 6 at night and got home filthy dirty and exhausted. And at the next meeting they would say: 'We made £150, and the kids can go to camp' and I would think 'Well, it was worth it all'. (I10, SW)

> Obviously people like to be liked and thought of as kind. People would say, 'Young Mrs B, she's a good soul'. It's nice when people say things like that about you. But firstly I did it because I wanted to. There's no way you would go out at 8 pm after a long day at work and come home at 10.30 if you didn't want to do it. I used to get so tired! (I10, SW)

Satisfaction also came from seeing how much the Scout movement had to offer children:

> Cubs gives them confidence – we run a six-system with a leader, a second and the younger ones below, so the older ones help the younger ones – you see their confidence building through this. And disabled children, they might have trouble with games, and if all the other Cubs are there cheering them on – it helps them so much in growing up, leadership experience, learning to co-operate – that is how society works, and it helps them to learn this from a younger age. (I3, SW)

> I was a Scout leader – my boys were in the Scouts and I wanted to give back something to the movement because they had gained from it – self-sufficiency, adventure. (I16, FW)

Another mother, who had not been involved in running the Scouts had still made contacts through taking her children there:

> When I first came here I met lots of mums through taking the children to Scouts. The Scout leader once gave my son a lift home when my husband forgot to collect him on time – they are helpful in that way. One feels that they get to know who you are, and would be willing to help if one needed it. (I6, SW)

The Scout movement in Sundon Park was still operating. However its popularity was declining among youngsters:

> Currently we have adequate adult help, but are down on children. (I3, SW)

I16's Scout group in Farley had disbanded altogether:

> The Scouts fizzled out because they didn't update, didn't give the boys what they wanted. Boys started to see it as too sissy. (I16, FW)

One mother commented that another reason for the growing weakness of the movement lay in the lack of broad-based community support for groupings of this nature. While parents were often happy to drop their children off and collect them, very few were willing to contribute time to organising and fund-raising activities:

> Our Cub parents will happily send their children to Cubs or to camp, but as soon as it comes to AGM time, or asking people to help you on the supporters' committee, or running jumble sales or sponsored walks, they don't want to know because they are going to have to do some work. So you end up with the same old crowd running things again and again. (I3, SW)

They were also less willing to attend fund-raising activities:

> Even when we hold social events, it's the same old faces that turn up, a small group of people building the community for everyone. (I3, SW)

3. Factors hindering involvement in voluntary organisations

A number of factors were cited as limiting people's involvement in voluntary organisations – relating to features of the community, features of people's lifestyles and features of the activities themselves. A number of features of the community deterred people from involvement: a *lack of trust*, particularly in Farley, both in terms of physical safety at night, as well as a perception that such activities often generated gossip. Farley had a council-run community centre which did offer a wide range of activities – including bingo, a youth club, exercise classes and playgroups for children. It also had a community caff, jointly run by the council and a group of volunteers:

> I would love to go to bingo at the community centre, but daren't walk around alone at nights. Groups of young lads – I'm frightened of them. (I8, FW)

> The community caff – I would never go there, bunch of gossip mongers . . . That's also why I avoid exercise classes at the community centre – I don't want everyone there to know that I want to lose weight and start talking about me. That's the way I think about community activities. (I4, FW)

> I don't think there is a community any more. Some people do meet in the community centre, or the community caff, but that's as far as it goes. All people do there anyway is slag off the council or slag off the neighbours. That's all that seems to happen up here. (I28, FM)

Particularly in Sundon Park, there were *limited places to meet and organise, as well as limited opportunities to meet* now that a growing number of women worked – often some distance away. Several Sundon Park people commented that their particular streets were deserted during the day, with more and more women going out to work, and people working increasingly greater distances from their homes. Sundon Park residents repeatedly bemoaned the lack of facilities in the area, in particular the lack of a community centre. Although there was a community centre in the Marsh Farm area of the ward, this was an area that most citizens in the ward sought to dissociate themselves from after the bad media publicity given to the area after a so-called 'riot'. They also avoided the area because they regarded it as dangerous.

It was partly the lack of social opportunities within Sundon Park that encouraged people to develop social and leisure links outside of the ward:

> It's boring here. You need a car. There's nothing going on in Sundon Park at all. (I33, SM)

> There's not a lot to do here socially. If we want to do something, we have to go out of Sundon Park. (I40, SW)

Older residents referred nostalgically to the Skefco social club, which had played a key role in the community until the Skefco factory had decided to close the club down to make way for offices. It was Sundon Park men in particular who bemoaned the passing of the club:

> We used to have a lovely social club but it's like everything else, nothing lasts for ever. That was a terrible crime when they closed their club, it broke all our hearts up here. (I25, SM)

> People up here don't knit much. I know so few of the people around here, I don't know the names of people in this very road, and we have lived here for yonks. You just don't meet people because there isn't a community hall, there's one pub, but it's not very close – and McDonald's. If there was like a club atmosphere – I mean there's not even bingo down here. Just to go now and again and have a quiet drink and a game of bingo – but there isn't. We could play darts or skittles or something like that.(I35, SM)

The Skefco club had been a meeting point for a number of male snooker enthusiasts, who now had to go out of the Sundon Park ward to find a replacement snooker venue.

Men in both wards spoke generally about a *decline in pub culture*. As we have seen, many people spoke of the role the local pub had played in their fathers' social lives. There had been a decline in pub culture over time. People these days were too busy to sit in pubs. Also the character of pubs had changed, as had the drink and drive laws:

> Pubs these days tend to cater for younger people, and they don't stay in one place long enough to knit together into a community. Also, since the drink driving laws people have got into the habit of going to the off-licence on the weekend and then getting a video – possibly that's not good for building community. (I36, SM)

Apart from this, as emerged in the focus groups, not only were there too few activities – there were often simply *inadequate networks to inform people about what was going on*. I36, who had lived in the ward for 37 years, said he had been surprised to find out how many activities there were:

> I was down in the library a few years ago, and the woman there told me some of the things that go on here. I was quite amazed like, cause there are lots of things for us older people to do. Not too much for the youngsters – but they go off and leave anyway. (I36, SM)

In addition people's lifestyles militated against community involvement, with a range of *competing demands* on those with families and financial responsibilities which made them too tired or busy to go out:

> I eventually gave up being Scout leader, it took up all my time, and my husband felt it was unfair, me going off all the time. I used to get into terrible trouble. I would come home from work and say I was going to the Scouts and my husband would say: 'Oh you're not going out again, are you?' so for doing good one got punished in a way. (I10, SW)

> I like greeting people, feeling I am growing in a community, knowing a little more about people. But I don't want any social side – don't want to spend a load of time in the evenings going to local meetings, and I don't have a lot of time during the day – what with working part-time, housework, seeing friends – I do like talking to friends, but when you do this you don't get anything else done. In the evening I think it is important that we all sit down and have a meal together, and then watch a bit of telly together before it's time for bed. If one of us had to go out to meetings on a regular basis it would take away from family life. There is an opportunity for me to go to church meetings on a Wednesday night – but I am too tired, and I don't want to go away from my family – I would rather stay at home. (I6, SW)

> I think times are hard, and people are so busy just surviving really a lot of the time – there's no time for community. (I24, FW)

One informant referred to the way in which the financial strain of negative equity deterred him and his family from attending any community activities at all, many of which involved payment of some sort, no matter how small:

> There are times recently when I have felt so fenced in by my problems that I don't know where to turn. It's like a pressure cooker needing release. When I was younger in London I had no trouble meeting people, because of being involved in the folk music world and all that. But when I got up here I had just bought the house and all I could afford to do was to pay the mortgage. At times we would toss up to pay the mortgage or buy food and often the mortgage won. There is no opportunity to go out, we can't afford to go out, we have almost become trapped in the house. (I5, FM)

It was often only older people with fewer responsibilities who had time to participate in community activities:

> When I was working so hard I was too tired to socialise with people in the community. Now that I am retired I am more lively. (I24, FW)

Because of this, involvement in community activity was sometimes seen, almost slightly scornfully by some, as the province of people who were lonely, or had nothing better to do. (A similar point has already been made on the basis of the focus group findings.)

Some who don't have such busy lives do more for the community because it is something to fill their lives, isn't it? I mean they are doing good, but not necessarily for the right reasons. (I24, FW)

I don't have time for community groups because I have a family, but there are obviously people that might be lonely, that lived alone, that might want more sort of social things. (I6, SW)

As will be seen in Chapter 7, younger adults often had little motivation to become involved in community networks that were dominated by pensioners.

Another factor that deterred people from becoming involved in local activities was the *negative image of the community* generated by sensationalistic media reporting which made people feel ashamed of the community (particularly in Sundon Park). Each ward had a particular incident. In Sundon Park, the Marsh Farm 'riots' a couple of years previously had received high coverage both nationally and internationally (one person referred to her son in Australia phoning her in alarm after the riots had featured on the Australian television news):

The riots were reported out of all proportion. I live here, and was here all the time they were going on outside my window, and at no stage through the riots did I feel there was any relationship between what I was hearing on the TV news and what I could see going on outside. (I11, SM)

A lot of things were reported that didn't actually happen. (I14, SM)

In Farley a fight outside the Parrot pub had also received widespread media attention. Negative reporting had a dampening effect on community morale, and people repeatedly said how dispiriting they found living in a place with a negative reputation. This undermined a sense of positive local identity, and made people less likely to be enthusiastic about community activities.

People also referred to a number of shortcomings of particular activities. They were sometimes dominated by cliques who made inadequate attempts to integrate newcomers:

I used to go to the church club with my neighbour, but we didn't feel happy there. Of the 30 ladies there were three groups of 10 who sat together and knew one another and you feel like an intruder. They talked to us, but we weren't sort of invited to join in and become part of them. We always felt like outsiders on our own, and eventually we dropped out. (I7, FW)

There weren't enough activities which appealed to *families*:

PTA activities, quiz nights, things like that – not well attended because men wouldn't want to go to those, and women don't want to leave their husbands at home. Whereas once when they did a treasure hunt, for the whole family, this was really well attended. (I6, SW)

This completes our discussion of the minimal role played by voluntary organisations (linked to leisure, hobbies and personal development) in the social networking of our informants in Farley and Sundon Park, as well as our attempt to highlight informants' explanations for the minimal nature of this involvement. The limited role of these groupings highlights an important limitation in the applicability of Putnam's notion of social capital to local communities in England, given the central role that such organisations play in generating those relationships of trust, reciprocity and local identity which form the backbone of his characterisation of the 'cohesive civic community'.

This chapter ends with a discussion of what we argue is a further limitation of Putnam's concept, that is his location of social capital within geographically bounded spaces. We argue that social capital is located within both narrower and wider spaces than the ward. Informants in both our wards emphasised that the street, or the close, were often the location of their most significant social networks. Informants in Sundon Park also referred to a range of networks that spilled well beyond the geographical ward boundaries. Much work remains to be done on the location of 'community'.

4. Geographical location of networks: the boundaries of 'community'?

Chapters 5 and 6 have looked at two types of community networks: informal networks of local friends and neighbours, and voluntary associations. At this stage we make some general comments about the extent to which these networks were located within the boundaries of the ward, and the extent to which involvement in them contributed to a sense of local identity.

As we have already seen in the focus group chapter (Chapter 3), while both Farley and Sundon Park residents regarded their ward as a pleasant place to live, there was a marked difference in the extent to which they felt any sense of local identity, with Farley residents expressing a strong sense of local belongingness compared to their Sundon Park counterparts. Sundon Park people said that the area lacked any kind of community heart or spirit, and was simply a place to live.

At first, the interview material on social networks did not throw any consistent light on this focus group finding. Accounts of *informal networks* in the two wards did not differ –

with residents of both wards talking about small exclusive networks of close neighbours and friends who offered one another help and support. Levels of involvement in *voluntary associations* of the types that Putnam refers to were low in both wards but, if anything, such involvement was higher in Sundon Park than in Farley. Levels of involvement in community-related activist networks were higher among Sundon Park residents than Farley residents (see Chapter 7 for further discussion of this point). At this level, the social network findings were suggestive of higher levels of community involvement in Sundon Park than Farley. This is exactly the opposite of what we might have expected in the light of the focus groups, in which Sundon Park residents expressed such low levels of local identity compared to Farley residents (which would have led us to expect far greater community involvement in Farley).

In response to explicit questions regarding whether or not they perceived Sundon Park to be a community, views were contradictory and inconsistent. For some, Sundon Park formed a very meaningful community:

> I've always felt that I had tremendous support from the community, people I have grown up with who still live around here. We all get on together and they are all there. People are so helpful, so many of them have a trade (one a gas fitter, one a sharpening business) so they are all there for each other, and there is always something that we can do for one another. (I40, SW)

For others there was no sense of community at all:

> There is no real feeling of community in Sundon Park. It feels quite isolated in a way. One is not aware of anyone or anything. No one will speak to each other. (I38, SM)

Others believed there might be a latent sense of community in Sundon Park, but this was only activated under unusual circumstances:

> I talk to everybody I can around here, but I don't think there is much community spirit. There might be if there was a train crash or something, people would gather together, but there is no general sense of togetherness I don't think. (I35, SM)

> There is generally no community spirit in Sundon Park, but then some does get shown on funny occasions. The aftermath of Diana dying, you saw that people around here cared. (I15, SM)

However more detailed attention to the interview material threw some light on the apparent contradiction in our findings regarding relatively low levels of community identity in Sundon Park, and relatively high levels of involvement in community networks.

Consistent with Putnam's notion of social capital as located within geographically bounded spaces, the social networks Farley people spoke of tended to be within the geographical ward boundaries. By contrast, the social networks that Sundon Park residents spoke of were either geographically wider or narrower than ward level:

- some informal friend–neighbour networks and all community activist networks (see below) tended to be located at the micro-level of the street, or at the level of a small group of people who had an interest in a particular and highly specific issue (that is narrower than ward)
- some informal friend–neighbour networks reached beyond the boundaries of Sundon Park, to friends and contacts in other geographical areas, as did much of what involvement there was in voluntary organisations (which also extended beyond ward boundaries).

In other words, the fact that Sundon Park residents did not express a sense of local identity did not mean that their involvement in networks was any less active than their Farley counterparts, but simply that the geographical ward played less of a role in the distribution of their networks.

In a range of ways, Sundon Park informants explicitly challenged the project's ward level and place-based conception of community. Sometimes they located community at the street level:

> If you asked me where my local community is, I wouldn't say Sundon Park. Rather I would say the immediately surrounding streets. (I26, SM)

> I wouldn't call Sundon Park as a whole a community. Community only exists in little local bits. (I35, SM)

> For me, the community is up this street. I get on well with most people in this street, it's generally a good neighbourhood to be in. (I33, SW)

> We have local identity in this street. The street is a small community in itself. Community has changed. People are becoming more introverted – there used to be wider community around here, but these days you only find it in little pockets, here, there and everywhere. (I39, SM)

> People live in Sundon Park, and that's all. I don't think they feel anything about it. It's not a chummy chummy, pally pally type place. Apart from having good neighbours there is no other contact. People don't say hallo to each other as a rule. (I27, SW)

Others explicitly rejected our assumption that communities inhered in geographical wards, on the grounds that they were more widely located.

In response to our question, what is a community, I40 (SW) had the following response:

> What is a community? It's the place where these are: your church, people you know, doctors and shops. (I40, SW)

But, for many Sundon Park people these networks lay beyond the geographical boundaries of the ward:

> For me, Sundon Park is an area rather than a community. I don't pay much attention to other people. But my doctor and health visitor are in another area where I used to live – I never changed – I have never thought of being part of a Sundon Park community. (I34, SW)

> There's no opportunity to be a community in Sundon Park with no community centre. If our children want to go anywhere they have to go out of the area. (I17, SW)

> Sundon Park is becoming less of a meaningful unit for me, especially now with the break-up of the local church, so I often don't go to the shops near here, but rather in the suburb where my new church is. There's nothing much here in the local shops anyway. (I3, SW)

I11 (SM), for example, had virtually no contact with neighbours or people in the geographical vicinity of Sundon Park. His choice of friends was conditioned by his particular interest in music:

> All my friends are interested in music. Listening or playing. Few of them live in Sundon Park. I'm in a band, I have two other guys who write music with me. I also sometimes teach music which involves going into schools or other environments. (I11, SM)

Many Sundon Park people chose to do their shopping in other areas, worked in other areas. Work networks – often beyond the immediate vicinity of residential wards – were also cited as important sources of social capital:

> It was awful retiring. What I got from working in that school was a sense of belonging, it was like a second home. I do my best to keep in touch with old work friends (I10, SW)

> Work life I consider to be social life. Going out to work gives you a chance to see a bit of life, to meet new people. I didn't like the actual firm at all, but it was the people I worked with that made it. (I17, SW)

I39 (SM) emphasised the dynamic and elastic boundaries of community life, which he said were determined more by situation than by area of residence:

> Our neighbours rent that house, the fourth set of neighbours in two years. There is constant disruption, noises, shouting, TV, music until the early hours of the morning. I've had to soundproof our bedroom wall and put a fence up to keep them out of our garden, which feels

sad. Anyway we leave them to get on with their lives and they leave us alone. So here you have a situation where people in a small space don't mingle at all. But when something like Princess Di's death happens, the whole nation feels it, the whole nation becomes a community because of one particular thing. So you can't say 'my community is here or there' or 'my community is this or that' – it's constantly changing, depending on the situation. (I39, SM)

In this ward we have friends that live around the area, the children have got many friends from school in the ward. And in actual fact I work with a man who lives in this ward – but I never see him other than at work which is some distance away. So you might have included him as part of my ward community, but I would put him in my work community and not my ward community. (I39, SM)

The sense of community lying beyond the boundaries of the ward was particularly strongly articulated by Sundon Park informants. We have already seen that there were very few local facilities in the area, and no widely accessible community centre. In Sundon Park there was a sense that inhabitants of this ward simply had wider horizons, a wider sense of possibilities than their Farley counterparts, a point that will be further developed in Chapter 7:

There is no sense of belonging any more, it's just another place these days. Such a moving population. People use Sundon Park as a stepping-off place. (I10, SW)

This finding resonates with the work of several community sociologists, such as Pahl (1995), who have long challenged the un-problematised assumption that communities are located within geographical boundaries. Our Sundon Park informants spoke of the dilution of place-based relationships and networks as social and living conditions were transformed by the increasing mobility, unpredictability and heterogeneity characteristic of life in the late twentieth century. They referred to this as a 'decline in community'. However detailed attention to their interviews suggested that while the social conditions they spoke of might have led to a decline in *place-based* community, they had also led to the development of *other* forms of community life – which cut increasingly across the more stable place-based boundaries of life. Strictly speaking what they were telling us about was more akin to a 'tranformation' of community than a 'decline' in community. In some ways, as already touched on in Chapters 3 and 4, Sundon Park residents appeared to have been more successful in adapting to the changing face of contemporary life, through creating networks and identities which transcended the growing limitations of the more narrowly place-based local communities of the past.

This was not necessarily the case in Farley. Farley residents also spoke of a 'decline in community' in the face of the increasing rapidity of social change – this was characterised in particular by a lack of trust, not only of those one did not know, but even sometimes of those one did know. Yet despite what people often described as a sense of growing alienation among community members people had continued to invest most of their identity in this small, local and relatively inward-looking place.

This preliminary finding has potentially interesting implications for health promoters concerned with enhancing levels of social capital within local communities – particularly given that several of the networks in our high-health community lay outside of the geographical boundaries of the Sundon Park ward. If social capital were indeed to become established as a tool for guiding local health promotion efforts, health promoters would not necessarily be able to assume that geographically defined local community identities existed as a resource for their work, or indeed that such identities were necessarily the most beneficial thing to aim for. Instead they might have to consider ways either of enhancing the development of wider networks and identities which spread across geographical boundaries (which might be too complex and expensive to do) or else to develop ways of promoting 'strategic alliances', that is attempting to create specifically issue-based identities in local places which bring together people from cross-cutting networks and identity groups around very specific and narrow issues of mutual interest (for example creating a common identity among an otherwise diverse group of local women around an issue such as sexual harrassment, or a particular children's health problem).

7. Civic engagement 3: Local activist networks and perceived citizen-power

The earlier chapters have examined the first two network types referred to in the interviews, that is informal and voluntary networks. Compared to Putnam's definition of social capital, voluntary networks play a relatively minor role in people's lives. This was in sharp contrast to informal networks which played the central role in the community life of our informants, yet do not feature in Putnam's conceptualisation of social capital at all. In other words, if it is to apply to local communities in England, we suggest that Putnam's typology of network types needs to be expanded to include informal networks, and the role which Putnam gives to voluntary organisations in the generating of community trust, reciprocity and identity needs to be somewhat de-emphasised.

Furthermore it was argued that, particularly in our high-health district of Sundon Park, the geographical location of such networks was not always consistent with our study's choice of geographical wards as the boundaries of what people subjectively experience as their community, with informal networks being at once narrower and broader than geographical ward-level boundaries. In addition, the relatively geographically dispersed nature of networks referred to by informants in Sundon Park, our high-health ward, lead us to suggest that such networks might be more health-enhancing than the geographically limited, inward-looking networks which characterised the community life of Farley residents in our sample.

This chapter turns to look at the third network type referred to by our informants, that is local community activist networks. In this chapter, we argue that this feature of social capital was the most effective in distinguishing between the communities of Farley (low health) and Sundon Park (high health). However we will specify that the role played by this form of social capital in people's lives often took an indirect form. It was not necessarily the case that large numbers of people were personally involved in these networks. Furthermore, those who did involve themselves in local activist issues often only became involved in particular single issue activities and for short periods of time, rather than in any sustained or long-term way. However, as we shall illustrate, the presence of these often very small-scale successful activist networks and groupings in the community generated an amorphous sense of what we shall call 'perceived citizen-power' – a belief in the power of ordinary people to influence local community life – which our pilot study suggests was the most important dimension of health-enhancing social capital in our high-health ward.

In the interviews people's accounts of such networks fell under the themes of: attitudes to politicians; attitudes to local government; participation in informal and formal community organisations and networks; and perceptions of citizenship. With regard to attitudes to politics and politicians at both the local and national levels there were no conspicuous inter-ward differences. There was an almost universal distrust of politicians. This involved both a cynicism about their motives, as well as a strong 'us–them' distinction between politicians and constituents. There was no sense in which our particular set of informants in either ward felt that politicians identified with their interests or had any sincere motivation to represent their needs. However, apart from this there were major differences in Sundon Park and Farley in people's attitudes to local government, and their perceptions of citizenship, and for this reason the extent and quality of involvement in community-oriented networks in each ward will be discussed in separate sections.

1. Farley: community-oriented networks

For Farley informants, politics had little relevance to their lives either at the local or the national levels. In the interviews a number of factors appeared to be linked to people's lack of interest in politics. These included:
• a satisfied or neutral attitude to local services;
• cynicism about politicians;
• negative experience of political involvement; and
• the perception that ordinary people have no power to influence the course of events, either at the local or the national level.
Each of these points is discussed in turn below.

Firstly – apart from the major complaint that the community lacked adequate leisure facilities and meeting places, particularly those for children and young people –

informants appeared to be *neutral or satisfied in their views of local government services*. However, this satisfaction represented the fact that people appeared simply to take them for granted, and did not have any particular views on them, positive or negative. The only informants who had views on local government and services were (two) informants who were having trouble with accessing benefits. It appeared that unless things went wrong people seldom thought about local government or community issues, either critically or otherwise.

While our interviews suggested that on the whole local government services tended to operate reasonably efficiently in routine situations in a faceless kind of way, people felt they had little joy when they tried to address muddles or to make legitimate queries with particular council personnel. These services were in the light of a client–provider model. There was no sense in which people felt that they had any active involvement or representation in the way in which such services were designed or provided. Furthermore, their attempts to complain on occasions where the services appeared to be functioning inefficiently almost inevitably met with frustration:

> Last year's doctor judged that I should stay off work. This year's doctor looked at exactly the same evidence and has judged that I no longer need income support. Now we have a long appeal, many hearings, I don't know what is going on. (I29, FM)

I28 (FM), a single father, spoke of his long struggle to get a stair-lift for his disabled child:

> The only way to get help from the council is to scream – with the welfare office at the town hall, or the housing office. If you just fill in forms and wait you never hear anything again. I wrote. Nothing. I phoned. Nothing. It's only when I shouted that I feel I'm getting somewhere. You've got to fight for every single little thing you want done, even the smallest little repair, you've got to fight. Keep on and on and on until they come and do it. (I28, FM)

> As far as getting anything from the social services or anything is concerned, I didn't get it. To get help from them you have to be a woman. They don't seem familiar with the notion of a single bloke looking after the kids. (I28)

Attempts to contact appropriate officials in the council often led to frustration:

> When I try and phone the council I spend 20 minutes listening to a bloody musical cassette, and then I usually get bored and hang up. That's a reflection of how interested they are – they don't want to know. (I21, FW)

Farley informants were virtually unanimous that politics was totally irrelevant to their lives. The second factor people cited for their reluctance to become involved in politics at the local or the national level was a *cynicism about politicians* – both in terms of their perceived lack of integrity and calibre, and more importantly in terms of informants' perceptions that politicians had little interest in representing the interests of their constituents. Firstly politicians were regarded as *ineffective*:

> Local politics is just a load of bullshit. It makes no difference to our lives. I have never seen a politician around here myself. They are totally ineffective and out of touch. (I21, FW)

Politicians were perceived as *greedy*. Several references were made to the point that politicians had raised their own salaries, despite the fact that so many ordinary people were battling financially:

> I resent fat cat politicians getting rich while we are ripped off left, right and centre. (I23, FW)

> My view of politicians? Totally and utterly disillusioned. They should all be taken out and shot. Everybody lies to get votes 'I'll do this, I'll do that' and then the first thing they do is put their own salaries up and we get nothing. (I28, FM)

They were also perceived as *dishonest*:

> Every time they hand out their pre-election manifesto pledges, it's like getting a new instalment of fiction. (I5, FM)

There was also a perception that politicians were *not concerned* about their constituents:

> I used to vote for a communist in local government when I lived in London. He was the only politician I ever knew of who was true to his beliefs, who really practised what he believed in. He actually went out and helped people. (I29, FM)

> Politicians are in it for themselves. Blair's got nothing to worry about – his wife earns more than he does, so he can afford to spend his time thinking about the country. (I32, FM)

Even those who were more sympathetic to politicians felt that their effectiveness was constrained by the lack of resources at their disposal:

> Politicians are always full of wonderful ideas, and then they get into power – and you know that they will never materialise because there is no money. I can appreciate why they change their views and ideas after they are elected, but basically I wouldn't put any confidence in them. (I21, FW)

The third reason offered for people's lack of involvement in local or national political networks was linked to *negative past experiences* of such involvement. In the focus groups, several Farley people referred to attempts they had made to express community views through involvement in petitions or fund-raising activities, eventually becoming despondent about such mobilising activities since they never seemed to bear fruit. In-depth interview participants also referred to having attended community meetings which they had regarded as a waste of time:

A few years ago I did go to a meeting about improving things on the estate, but it wound up with everyone just bitching about irrelevant things. I just got up and walked out and didn't bother after that. (I28, FM)

We tried attending a community meeting about a local problem once and it never works. There was a fight between an Asian boy and a white boy which led to a big conflict, and when the police held a meeting they refused to look at what had started the problem. They weren't allowed to talk about whites and Asians fighting because it would 'sound racist'. Too many do-gooders and not enough sense. The police's hands are tied by higher authority. (I28, FM)

As will be discussed below, the Sundon Park Residents' Association played a central role in Sundon Park informants' accounts of community life. Only one person referred to the Farley Tenants' Association in a positive way:

There is a Farley Tenants' Association, that do a lot of work trying to improve the community, and all the local counsellors live on the estate which means they are approachable and accessible. The tenants' association has got the community café going, they have given people a place where they can come together and have a cup of tea. Also they are the movers behind getting a housing office on the estate. I don't have anything to do with the tenants' association because I'm a home owner, but for council tenants it means that they have a local voice. They can actually physically change things. (I5, FM)

Others were aware of the existence of the association, and felt that its existence was a good thing, but would not have considered involving themselves:

There is nothing local. They never write and ask you to join things for the children, for example. I would like to see a group set up for residents – a group which had meetings, tried to help the children – or families which needed help. Build a little club, organise football for the boys. (I23, FW)

I23 was unaware of the tenants' association's existence:

I don't think we have anything like that [a tenants' association]. It's very hard to get anything done here. They keep saying they are going to do this, and going to do that . . . people would like to do something but there is no one to help them. I think people just stick with each other in the end, rather than getting involved with local issues. (I23, FW)

The groups and activities of which she speaks do, in fact, exist in Farley:

Fourthly and finally, Farley informants shared the perception that *ordinary people had no power to influence the course of events*. Here it must be emphasised that this lack of faith in the political process was not presented as a criticism of particular politicians in Luton, or articulated in relation to particular political parties (although a number of respondents did point to the role that 'eighteen years of Thatcherism' had played in undermining community spirit in the UK) – but rather in terms of a deep cynicism about the intrinsic power of any aspect of local or national government to reflect the needs, interests and views of ordinary working-class citizens in England. This lack of what we refer to in this report as 'perceived citizen-power' had a number of dimensions.

Apathy and a 'culture of moaning': Some people spoke of apathy or 'laziness' as factors deterring people from community involvement. Certain of the informants that were most vociferous in their criticism of local government and community affairs were ironically simultaneously the least interested in getting involved. I4 herself pointed to this contradiction in her narrative as the interview progressed:

> I am boring, aren't I? It's just that I moan that there isn't anything for the kids or teenagers to do, but I'm not willing to do anything about it. If everybody thinks like I do and nobody wants to get involved, then there's never going to be anything here, is there? (I4, FW)

Several people expressed apathy about community involvement:

> I have often found that I am full of great ideas, but then when it sort of comes to saying to myself 'Well I could go to that meeting and put forward my opinion', I say to myself, 'No, what will happen is that I will get roped into something I don't really want to do.' (I5, FM)

> I have never felt strongly enough about an issue to actually go to the council or an MP. (I5, FM)

> We always know what's going on in the community because I get their free letters and that. As for taking part I'm sorry to say that I am no good at that. I am not into politics – a combination of laziness and no time. I have never really been politically motivated. (I9, FM)

> A lot of people can't be bothered to do things for the community, because they don't have the energy. (I12, FM)

> It's unlikely that I would have any interest in getting involved in community-building activities. I might sign the odd petition for traffic calming, but nothing more. I can't think of any activities that might appear. I can't think of anything more awful than a street party, for example (I21, FW)

> I'm not interested in community activities. They don't do anything interesting. (I4, FW)

Lack of perceived citizen-power: This apathy resonated with Farley residents' view that ordinary people did not have much power to have any impact on community life or decision-making:

> I don't contact officials or politicians because I don't feel I have any power to actually change anything. (I5, FM)

> People aren't interested in the affairs of Farley. Most of us are single mums battling to survive. We have our personal worries to deal with – politics is very distant – nothing ever happens for our good in politics anyway. (I23, FW)

I21 was the only Farley woman informant who reported on a family history of political involvement. She said that her grandfather had been involved in a popular protest against a Luton mayor and his way of managing money – which had culminated in the town hall being set alight:

> It didn't make the blind bit of difference burning down the town hall. The mayor was still the bloody mayor, and he could still do what he bloody wanted, and that was the difference. (I21, FW)

I22 knew one person who had attempted to become involved in politics:

> There was a lass who lived down towards the corner shop who did stand for council once, and get in, but she found that good intentions don't get you very far . . . after a year or two she had enough of it and gave up. (I22, FW)

> It doesn't matter who you have got in government, they are going to give you the biggest load of bullshit out. Nobody is going to do anything anyway. It doesn't matter where you put your cross on the ballot paper, you're going to get what they are going to give you and you've just got to make the most of it. (I21, FW)

Women's particular lack of interest in politics: Perceived lack of citizen-power was particularly pronounced in many female interview respondents who defined politics as a male domain and one that lay beyond their interest or ability to understand:

> I always keep my politics to myself – but you do get the men discuss it – 'I'm right, you're wrong' discussions, that sort of thing . . . women don't discuss politics. They talk more about kids and decorating and all those chores they haven't done that they should be doing. (I23, FW)

> I don't vote. I'm not interested. I just let everybody else vote for me. (I30, FW)

Several of those who did vote said that they had been guided by husband or father in their choice of candidate:

> Dad's always been a Labour man, so I had to go for Labour in the end. (I23, FW)

> I don't understand politics. My husband said vote Labour, so I vote Labour. Men have more interest and understanding of these things than women. Women are usually tied up with children and everyday living and they don't bother too much about that side of it, they just lean on their husbands and are swayed by them. (I7, FW)

In summary, involvement in community-related activist groups or initiatives in Farley was minimal. On the one hand this was ascribed to a general satisfaction with, or neutrality towards, the routine delivery of services, which meant that there were few widely and strongly held grievances about services that might have galvanised people into united action. (Although some individuals had bitter complaints about isolated problems relating to services and benefits, these complaints were diffusely spread over a spectrum of issues.)

Several other factors were also relevant to these low levels of involvement. There was evidence for negative attitudes towards politicians and the political process in general, negative experiences of past attempts to become involved in meetings or activities aimed at community improvement, and a lack of perceived citizen-power (particularly strong among women, many of whom defined politics as a male domain). This lack of faith in the power of ordinary citizens to influence community events went hand in hand with a general community culture where people often moaned but seldom acted. Farley residents in our sample tended to have had little or no experience of political involvement either within the community or outside of it (for example in work-related trade unions).

2. Sundon Park: community-oriented networks

In some respects, the attitudes of Sundon Park informants to community/political issues was not very different to those of their Farley counterparts. They were also uninterested in involving themselves in formal politics at the local or national levels. One reason they offered for this was their general satisfaction with the level of local government service provision. Another was their distrust of politicians.

However there were three distinct differences between the wards. The first lay in people's perceptions of citizen-power. Sundon Park had a thriving voluntary residents' association which was seen by many of the residents as a credible and representative voice for community residents. Secondly, unlike Farley, Sundon Park informants referred to several examples of successful community-based projects and activism. Thirdly the attitude of Sundon Park women to politics was very different. As we have seen, several Farley women explicitly excluded themselves from community and political action through delineating these as male realms of focus, with others simply saying that they had no understanding or interest in politics. Such sentiments were not expressed by women in Sundon Park, several of whom had actively involved themselves in community issues. Those who had not been actively involved said that this was because they were too busy with other activities to do so, but that they might consider more active involvement when their children had grown up, or when they had more time. Some expressed regret that they were not more active (which did not happen with women in Farley). Not one woman said she lacked interest in or understanding of community affairs.

Each of these issues is discussed in turn.

Satisfaction with local services: On the whole people seemed relatively satisfied with the quality of local services and the way in which the Sundon Park community was run:

> The problem is that I am a bit complacent. I am satisfied – they [*the council*] try – parking, waste bins, all the things we complain about get done. Nursery classes, the drop-in community shop. This is generally an easy place to live, like everyone else if an issue does not affect me I leave it alone. (I10, SW)

> I might get involved in community activities if they related to children's safety or snooker – but on the whole I am quite contented with life here, so I wouldn't be motivated to get involved in any community politics. (I14, SM)

Because the council seemed to run things fairly smoothly, people were not very aware of their existence:

> I don't have a lot to do with the council. They take our tax, and come and collect the bins on Friday. (I27, SW)

People had seldom sought help from local authority bodies, seldom contacted local officials, seldom got together with others to solve local problems – although on occasions where problems had arisen they agreed the council had been responsive. And those who had not had problems were aware of the fact that it was possible for community members to express their views:

> I pay no attention to the council – but if I had a strong view on something I would let them know. (I34, SW)

Even those who were a little more critical of the council expressed this in a fairly tolerant and easy-going way:

> Things could be better – sports facilities, community centre, better public transport, road calming – but one has to live in a realistic world. (I6, SW)

And people accepted that they had some potential contribution to make to the way in which the council delivered services – a theme that will be elaborated on below:

> They have a hard job to do, but I just feel sometimes I could do it better. But I should get myself on the residents' association, so I'm just as much to blame. (I40, SW)

As was the case in Farley, despite the fact that benefit and service delivery functioned well enough in routine situations, people often felt completely powerless in non-routine situations. Thus, for example, several Sundon Park women had experienced postnatal depression. One had sought help from her mother. Another had been referred by her GP to a 'Meet a Mum' support group of women with similar problems. A third, however, had just suffered on her own when she developed post-miscarriage depression, reluctant to access the source of help the hospital had recommended:

> When people need help for emotional problems, they really have to search for it. I had a miscarriage, and they gave me a phone number to call if I was upset. I would have been terrified to phone a stranger about something so painful. If the community had a health visitor available at all times there would be a familiar face, someone you could easily approach. If help was more easily available, people would not carry on suffering on their own; if you have to search for something you are less likely to try than if it is easily accessible. (I34, SW)

Another woman spoke of her protracted battle to get treatment for her child who she believed had a learning disability/attention deficit problem. One doctor after another had insisted there was nothing wrong with him, she felt trapped by her inability to explain and demonstrate the nature of the problem to them in the short time doctors allocated to patients, and it was over a year before she could get anyone to take the problem seriously:

> I have been through such heartache with this child. Doctors kept on saying there was nothing wrong with him. It's been a battle to get as far as we have got in getting him treated, and we are now only starting to scratch the surface of the problem. If you are a layman you don't know the terms, and you can't explain yourself to a doctor in the five minutes he has for you – where the child is just sitting beside you, and the doctor can't see the problem. It was only after he went to a speech therapist who spent two hours with him, and she agreed that there was something wrong with him, and that he ought to be referred – I had been saying this to doctors again and again for more than a year. (I6, SW)

Negative attitude to politicians: Farley informants' attitudes to politicians had been almost unambiguously negative. Sundon Park residents' attitudes to politicians were more varied. Some were negative:

> There doesn't seem to be much community spirit here. The only time we see a counsellor is when they come and knock on the door and ask for your vote. We had Mr —— here last time . . . he didn't get voted back in. I had only seen him twice in twelve years, even when we tried to see him, we couldn't. (I35, SM)

> Politicians were in the community only a week or so ago. Someone called K—— came to my door. I had never seen him before, and I haven't heard of him since. It's sad. He had time for the community that week, but not since. It would be fairly easy. If I had his power, if he was really interested in finding out what this community's problems were, he need only come and ask. (I11, SM)

> Ha ha – politicians think about their jobs first, don't they? Nurses and teachers get about a 3 per cent pay rise, and then they give themselves about 25 per cent. (I25, SM)

Others were more sympathetic:

> They do often say one thing and then do another. But I suppose one needs to have a certain amount of trust – they do have a hard job. (I13, SM)

> They are well meaning – in spite of the fact that the promises they make about what they are going to do always make things sound grander than they turn out in practice. (I14, SM)

On the whole however, despite a slightly more positive attitude to politicians, none of our Sundon Park informants had any inclination to become politically active:

> I don't want to be involved in politics, it's not relevant to my life. (I13, SM)

However despite their antipathy to political or community involvement at the local or national government level, Sundon Park informants showed evidence of a more confident perception of the power of citizens to take control of issues at the local community level. People were very familiar with the notion of community activism at a local level, and aware of the benefits of this action.

Perceptions of citizen-power: Like their Farley counterparts, perceptions of citizen-power were not strongly articulated at the level of local or national political issues, apart from one person who said it was important to 'fight for one's rights', and two others who referred positively to the success of the popular protests against the poll tax – in ways that suggested the rudiments of belief in the power of ordinary people to assert themselves in the political arena:

> If my child was ill and not getting the right services I would fight for the fact that my child should get proper public health care. I am one of the people who would shout. You see lots of people who won't shout. If the health authority says the treatment is not available for their child, they just say OK and walk away. They don't realise they can actually get it. There are ways in which they can, they are entitled to it, and I'm just one of those people who believes this. (I11, SM)

> The only time I can think of people influencing politics was the poll tax, all of these people raising up and they eventually got rid of it. (I35, SM)

People expressed some faith in citizen-power in two more limited contexts, however. The first of these included numerous references (particularly by women) to little victories that Sundon Park citizens had achieved at the micro-community level; the second was existence of the ward's local residents' association.

These small battles included relatively 'easy' achievements such as individuals lobbying the council to repair play equipment in the park; approaching the council to put bollards at the end of a local footpath to slow down children on bicycles who had been endangering pedestrians; persuading the council to build a pedestrian path along a muddy grassy walkway beside a busy road. These little victories had engendered a great sense of satisfaction among residents:

> Well I got that path put in on the main road, see it over there – it's mine! [*laughter*]. There is no speed limit and a country road comes into the area, so people fly down here. I got caught one night and hit my elbow as a car came speeding round the bend. You had to walk in the grass and the mud to avoid them. I complained and they came around and inspected it and put that tarmac down. (I17, SW)

They also included more labour intensive lobbying such as collecting signatures for a petition to the council regarding a resident who was inconveniencing others in the street by keeping a large bulldozer parked outside his house. An even more significant and successful achievement was the year-long campaign mounted by I40 against a local peanut factory which was causing a public nuisance with noise and smell:

> I found through chatting to neighbours that they were all complaining to the council separately, ringing or writing, about the sickening smell from the factory, so I pulled the whole thing together. I said, we need to have someone co-ordinating this, otherwise it's ineffective all doing things off our own bat. So I wrote to the Environmental Health Officer who came out. I paid someone to come and do recordings of the noise, then we went and annoyed our local MP who

was very sweet. I was the spokesperson pulling it all together, writing, monitoring, sending out little photocopied sheets to let people know what was going on. This went on for about a year, but it worked – they sorted out the peanut factory. (I40, SW)

I went from door to door and asked people if they were finding the factory a problem. I knew a few people, and those I didn't know I just got chatting to, and people don't mind sort of chatting to you. I got them to put down their names, those people who had been disturbed by the noise, and what time it was. Because I thought that with people like that you have got to let them know that you mean business, and you have got to keep on and be consistent about it. It did do some good. It just let them know that we really meant business and we were fed up with it and concerned enough to do something about it . . . a fresh face coming and pulling together everyone's complaints and writing – I think people around here appreciated that. (I40, SW)

I40 outlined how this experience had taught her a range of lobbying skills, and it had clearly given her a positive sense of active citizenship:

The trick is to follow the chain of command rather than trying to go straight to the top. If you don't get joy from one person, go to the next one up, and just keep going, go on keeping on – and you can get things done. You can change things in that way – people do that around here, and succeed. (I40, SW)

The local authority man was very helpful and gave me his phone number and if ever I had problems again I should phone him immediately and they were monitoring the problem. So he did seem genuinely helpful, and interested. I always feel I can go to them if I need to. (I40, SW),

However, the experience of mounting this successful campaign around a single issue which affected her and her family personally, did not translate into any desire to become involved in broader community issues:

After this had worked so well, they asked me to go on the residents' association, but I know I'm not committed enough – if I am going to do that you really have to give it your all. You have to be passionate about it, it's not worth doing it half-heartedly. I am happy to do what I do, but not in a formal way. (I40, SW)

I27 spoke of a campaign to stop big lorries from using her road. Although she too portrayed this as a strictly one-issue campaign, it had clearly left her with a sense of empowerment as a Sundon Park resident:

We whipped up a big storm and got the newspapers to come in, because we didn't want our children to be hurt by the big lorries going to the building site. We also had petitions and everything. And we did it – we won – then we all got back into our little houses and hid! But it's amazing what you can do if you work in a united way. (I27, SW)

Attempts to get involved in community action were not always easy. I6 spoke of the difficulties facing ordinary people who sought to organise community activities. In particular she pointed to the lack of networking between the PTA and the school:

> It's difficult to organise things at the local level without organisational back-up – things like access to computers and photocopiers. On the PTA, for example, one sometimes feels it's separate from the school – the school wants the PTA, but doesn't want us to use the classrooms for the meetings, or to borrow their copier.

> When you try and set up a group really you are on your own – you don't get support from the council or anyone, this problem puts people off organising things – having to hand-write twenty notices for a mothers' coffee morning group because you don't have access to a computer, this all take a lot of time we don't have. Community things rely on people who are willing to give up an awful lot of time to do them. (I6, SW)

> I often think if ever I were on my own there is so much I could get involved with in the community – one need never be lonely – but it's obviously getting into that, getting accepted in a community that might be difficult – I mean, I could go and help at the school – they are crying out for helpers, but probably if I didn't have children they would be suspicious of why I wanted to help out in the school. So I can see how you would be quite nervous if you were on your own, to go in and ask to do something like that – in case you were rejected. (I6, SW)

> I got involved in the 'Meet a Mum' grouping and it was really difficult in those first meetings – when you were a new person in, you didn't know what to say, what to do. It's difficult to take the first step in talking to people. (I6, SW)

The other difficulty – mentioned by virtually every Sundon Park respondent in the interviews and focus groups – was the lack of what people considered an accessible community centre or meeting place.

A link between community action and an increase in personal self-efficacy was made directly in one informant's reference to setting up a Neighbourhood Watch in her street – referred to in a far more positive way than it was in our Farley interviews:

> A woman in our street has started a Neighbourhood Watch. She says she wants something to do – her children have gone away to university, and she's not in a job at the moment. She wants to start organising things to bring her back into an employable state. She also wants to get the benefits of having a Neighbourhood Watch – cheaper house insurance, decreased risk of burglary – as well as it helping us to get to know each other, and becoming a closer community. (I6, SW)

The residents' association featured strongly in our Sundon Park interviews. None of our informants was actively involved in it, attitudes to the association ranged from extremely positive to the negative, and none of our informants mentioned any concrete victories it had achieved on behalf of its members. Despite this, it was a constant reference point in people's accounts of their day-to-day lives in the community. They clearly appreciated the fact that there was a local forum which had their interests at heart:

> I'm a member, though I have never been to a meeting, but they send us their newsletter, and I think they do a very good job. (I17, SW)

> I have heard it is quite active, but don't know anybody in it. It's nice to know that it exists. I haven't got the time to do it myself, but it feels good that there's a residents' association looking out for things in the community and some of the things they have done are good – like their fight to keep the library open. The kids are my life at the moment, but as they get older I hope there will be more time to be involved. (I34, SW)

> We have a couple of locals on the residents' association, and they keep us informed about what is going on. Particularly T——, he's very passionate about it – he has seven children and is always busy, but he still finds time to do it. He's very knowledgeable about what is going on in the area. It's important to have people like that to pull it all together and to help people out. (I40, SW)

> We have got a very good residents' association. They are currently fighting for a community centre for us. (I10, SW)

> Part of Sundon Park has got quite good areas, we don't get a lot of crime here, and there is a local community association. The residents' association have a little office and I know a lot of people involved. Personally I don't get involved in it, but I know it's there if I wanted to. We get to know a lot of things from knowing quite a few people in the area, my wife knows a lot more, she's more outgoing and knows all the people in the road, which I don't. (I36, SW)

People were not uncritical of the resident's association. Some felt the grouping had got somewhat 'stale' due to too many long-standing elderly members:

> It could do with livening up. It's a group of elderly people and they have been doing it for so long – I think that it's lost its impetus, with the same people in it for years and years. It really needs more younger people and people with children. (I3, SW)

Others commented that in the final analysis a small local association was powerless in the face of government decisions:

> I pay an annual fee to belong, and I do think it's a good idea. I should try and attend the meetings more and find out what is happening. Honestly, I don't think they have got a lot of power as far as I can see because they say they are not going to allow this or that (for example

the construction of a big roundabout), but it's still put there because the government say they want to have one. (I13, SM)

The residents' association don't have a lot of power, not what I can see. They say they are not going to allow this or that and it still gets done because the government overrides them again and again. (I13, SM)

Others commented on the relative power of big business:

They tried to stop people from building a factory – the only way they could do it was to buy the land and they asked for £1.5 million for it. They tried to get the money from the National Lottery, but it was too late, they have already started building the factories. (I39, SM)

The association was also often powerless in the face of council opposition:

There's not much the residents' association can do. They have to get past the council first, haven't they? They've been wanting to build a community centre but haven't got funds, so they started collecting money for this – but how long is it going to take them to save what's needed – it won't happen in their lifetimes. (I25, SM)

But despite a range of criticisms, there was a general feeling that all good citizens should be involved in this grouping, and people were often slightly embarrassed by their lack of commitment:

Some of us are a bit complacent really, I am too, I'm ashamed to say. It doesn't affect me, I leave it alone, which is quite selfish really. (I10, SW)

My friend C—— is very active in the residents' association. If he ever needed help to do something I would do it. I would be interested in that way, but I wouldn't go out of my way to get involved. He's a good leader. Some people are leaders and others just do what they are told. I'm like that. That's the trouble – there are too many of us that just sit back and do nothing. I must admit I am guilty of that. (I26, SM)

We don't have time to get involved in the residents' association. We are a bunch of miserable buggers, aren't we? Anti-social really. (I39, SM)

I should do more for the community, but time is the problem. (I36, SM)

Experience of political involvement outside the community: Here it must be emphasised that what community action did exist in the ward related to micro-issues that affected people directly. People did not make any links between these small acts of mobilisation and broader political issues. Apart from these small local issues, Sundon Park people tended to be apolitical. Thus although eight of our male Sundon Park informants had been trades union members at some stage of their lives, and spoke vaguely of union membership as being 'worthwhile', this did not seem to have served as a politicising force in any informant's life, neither did they link union memberships with any political, community or personal issue beyond the limits of workplace matters.

Women and politics: As opposed to Farley women, many of whom said that they would not become politically active either because they did not understand politics or else because they regarded politics as a male sphere, Sundon Park women often had more positive reasons for their lack of involvement. The first was to do with time and the competing demands of family life:

> I have no time to involve myself in community meetings – I put my children's education first – at night I try and get them to read things to me, I would like to think that when they are older I will have more time for non-family things. (I27, SW)

> I have enough to do without belonging to a political party. (I17, SW)

The second was to do with competing community commitments:

> My work in the church and in the Scouts is more meaningful for me. I can have more impact on the community at this level. I don't think that I could have that impact through a local political group. (I3, SW)

3. Involvement in community activist networks in Farley and Sundon Park: similarities and differences

In analysing attitudes to, and involvement in, local community-linked networks and initiatives in our two wards of interest, the following themes dominated: trust in politicians (low in both wards); satisfaction with local services (reasonably high in both wards); perceptions of citizen-power – including the presence of credible representative organisations, and a collective memory of successful community activism (high in Sundon Park, low in Farley); the extent of the links which people made between the personal and political dimensions of existence (low in both wards, slightly higher in Sundon Park); the extent to which people viewed good citizenship in an active, community-linked way or a passive and personalised way (passive and personalised in both wards); and women's view of politics as a male domain (which was the case in Farley, but not Sundon Park).

The in-depth interviews supported the focus group finding that Sundon Park informants had a stronger sense of the potential power of ordinary citizens to make their voices heard on community-related matters that had an impact on their lives. In the interviews this increased sense of 'perceived citizen-power' emerged in relation to accounts of more frequent and more successful complaints or mini-campaigns by ordinary people to bring about minor and small-scale community improvements, more frequent references to the local residents' association and a relative confidence by women to hold views on local issues, or even to take action on them from time to time.

Here it must be emphasised that what 'political' involvement had taken place in Sundon Park was restricted to minor issues at the micro-community level – and related only to matters that had had an immediate and direct effect on people's day-to-day perceptions of their safety and wellbeing. There was no evidence that it had translated into any broader political commitment or to more generalised participation in other community issues. Nor had it translated into a stronger perception of the personal–political link than had been held by the Farley informants. However, what it had translated into was a grassroots sense of citizen-power – not only among both those who had been actively involved in mini-campaigns or residents' association activities – but also among those who were aware that other local citizens ('people just like us') had succeeded in making their voices heard on issues that concerned them.

A future research instrument examining social capital in local communities in England would need to develop a measure of 'perceived citizen-power', which took account not only of people's actual involvement in actions to solve local problems (and whether or not these had been successful), but also of involvement of people known to informants. It would also need to take account of the extent to which informants or people known to them had complained about local issues, as well as the extent to which such complaints had been successful. In addition it would need to differentiate between gendered perceptions of these issues, focusing specifically on women's perceptions of the extent to which they had the interest or ability to understand political issues.

4. Civic engagement: conclusion

Chapters 5, 6 and 7 have examined the three different types of networks referred to by in-depth interview informants: informal face-to-face networks, voluntary associations and community-linked networks. In contrast to Putnam's definition of social capital in terms of voluntary associations and community-level networks, densely interfaced with government-provided institutions and facilities, the community resources drawn on by our informants took a far more informal and interpersonal form. Levels of trust and reciprocity among members of these informal interpersonal networks were robust – with members offering one another varying degrees of emotional and instrumental support and friendship – but these positive relationships did not usually extend more broadly than these narrow and exclusive networks (compared to Putnam's specification of identity and trust as a quality of relationships that extended beyond personal acquaintances to a broader range of community members). The only exception to the location of trust within interpersonal networks arose in the case of emergencies or accidents, where most informants in both wards said that strangers would offer one another appropriate and positive aid. On the whole, voluntary associations of the type that Putnam refers to played a relatively minor role in people's lives, as did community-based networks.

There were three major differences between networks referred to by informants in Farley and Sundon Park. Firstly Sundon Park informants tended to be involved in a broader array of networks than their Farley counterparts. Secondly both informal and voluntary networks referred to by Sundon Park informants tended to extend over a broader geographical area than those referred to by Farley informants. Thirdly there was evidence for greater levels of civic engagement in Sundon Park – albeit that such engagement tended to take place around minor issues at the micro-community level, related only to issues that had an immediate and direct effect on people's daily lives, and did not translate into any broader political commitment or more generalised interest in broader community issues. Despite the limited nature of this civic engagement, it had resulted in a stronger sense of grassroots citizen-power in Sundon Park than in Farley, not only among those who had been directly involved in community-based networks and initiatives, who tended to be a minority, but also among those who were aware that other local citizens ('people just like us') had succeeded in making their voices heard on issues concerning them.

The focus groups have already pointed towards higher levels of perceived citizen-power among Sundon Park informants. This focus group finding, together with in-depth interview evidence for higher levels of civic engagement in Sundon Park, suggest that high levels of civic engagement, together with high levels of perceived citizen-power, are important aspects of health-enhancing social capital.

The findings reported in this chapter showed that our choice of geographically bounded wards as our unit of analysis resonated only partially with people's subjective accounts of their significant social networks. These networks were at once narrower (in both areas) and broader (particularly in Sundon Park) than the boundaries of geographical wards. We have pointed to the potentially complex implications of this for those who seek to implement health promotion programmes and policies at the local community level.

8. Conclusion

This study has taken place within the context of a gap in the field of health promotion research. In our literature review we commented that although much research has explored correlations between macro-social factors (for example gender, socioeconomic status) and health, and between a range of psycho-social processes (for example self-efficacy, social support) and health, far less is known about the links between health and community-level relationships and networks. This gap in knowledge is particularly problematic in the light of the recent shift within health education and promotion. This has involved a move away from persuading individuals to change their behaviour through the provision of information about health risks, towards an interest in creating community contexts that are most likely to enable health-promoting behaviours to occur.

This study has been the first exploratory step in a continuing research programme which explores the potential of the concept of social capital to fill this gap. In it we have explored the possibility that social capital might serve as a useful conceptual tool for pinpointing those aspects of local community life which enable or support health-enhancing behaviours, and/or reduce the negative health consequences of the stresses of daily living. Within the context of political science, Putnam (1993a) has defined social capital as the community cohesion resulting from high levels of civic identity and the associated phenomena of trust, reciprocity and civic engagement. We have hypothesised that there is a link between social capital and health, and that local health promotion projects should seek to enhance levels of social capital in the interests of creating community contexts that enable and support health-enhancing behaviours, and serve as a buffer against health-damaging strain and stress.

The goals of this study have been twofold. Firstly the aim has been to investigate the form that social capital takes in local communities in England, and the extent to which Putnam's definition of social capital resonates with ordinary people's experience of community life. If health promoters are to seek to promote social capital in local communities it is important that they have a clear idea of the nature of the communities in which they work, and a clear understanding of the resources that exist as a starting point for this task. Secondly the aim has been to examine differences in the forms and levels of social capital in our high-health and low-health wards, in the interests of highlighting which aspects of social capital might be more or less important for health promotional programmes and policies.

Putnam's concept of social capital has provided a useful starting point for our exploratory study of local communities in England. In this section we point to seven tentative findings of our pilot study. These findings flag up several promising directions for future research by those concerned with health promotion in local communities in England.

1. Certain dimensions of Putnam's social capital (particularly trust and civic engagement/perceived citizen-power) might be more health-enhancing than others.
Our exploratory study has pointed to variations in the levels of different dimensions of social capital in our low-health and high-health wards of interest. We argue for the need to disaggregate the concept of social capital. It is our belief that certain dimensions of community cohesion might be more health-enhancing than others.
- The dimension of *reciprocal help and support* did not serve to distinguish our high-health and low-health communities. Help and support between exclusive networks of neighbours and friends appeared to exist in both wards.
- The phenomena of *trust, perceived citizen-power* and *civic engagement* were higher in our high-health community than in our low-health community.
- Contrary to our hypothesis the dimensions of *local identity* and *local facilities* were higher in our low-health community. (Both these points are taken up below.)

2. Sources of social capital often cross the boundaries of geographically defined communities.
Our interviews suggested that we need to broaden the geographical scope of our research into social capital, and that the networks constituting the social capital of many of our informants were both local and non-local in nature. While a large number of the networks people referred to tended to be micro-locally based, often at the level of the street, or within easy walking or short driving distance from one another, some networks crossed the boundaries of the geographical ward, with people being involved in a range of activities and networks lying outside its boundaries. The starting assumption of our study, examining social capital at the level of the geographical ward, was unduly narrow in its approach. Future studies should take account of the fact that people's stocks of social capital reside in a range of non-local as well as local networks and associations.

3. Certain network types (diverse and geographically dispersed) might be more health-enhancing than others.
Not only should we take account of the fact that people's stocks of social capital include

both local and non-local networks. We have also argued that a broader range of networks might be associated with higher-health outcomes. Thus, for example, the relatively strong local identity reported in our low-health ward might not be as paradoxical as it first appeared. A strong local identity could arguably even be a marker of low social capital insofar as it suggests that people have access to a relatively restricted range of social capital/networks. By the same token, the relatively weak local identity reported in our high-health ward might indicate that informants in this ward had access to a geographically wider array of networks from which they derived their social identities. In this regard, health researchers could learn much from the growing sociological literature on the advantages and disadvantages of various network forms.

4. Putnam's typology of social networks needs to be expanded, and in particular more attention needs to be paid to informal networks.

In his definition of social capital, Putnam (1993a and b) lays emphasis on the importance of high levels of involvement in voluntary associations and organisations (such as literary societies and bowling leagues) which he argues should interlock with state-provided services and facilities. Our research highlighted three network types: informal interpersonal networks (referred to by informants in both wards), voluntary associations (seldom referred to in either ward) and community-linked activist groupings and initiatives (referred to in our high-health ward only).

- Networks in both our wards of interest were restricted overwhelmingly to the interpersonal type. Such networks tended to be informal in nature, and highly exclusive insofar as their membership was tightly restricted to people who were personally acquainted with one another. More attention needs to be paid to the small-scale, *informal networks of friends and neighbours* which formed the bulk of the social capital available to informants in both our wards.
- *Voluntary associations* of the type that Putnam refers to were rare in both our communities of interest (even more so in our low-health ward), and the few voluntary associations that did exist rarely had interlocking relationships with state-provided services and facilities of the kind that Putnam refers to.
- Virtually no reference was made to *community-level networks* in our low-health ward. Informants in our high-health ward referred to the existence of a representative residents' association as well as a range of successful examples of small-scale community activism. These phenomena played a central role in the accounts people gave of community life in our high-health ward. They were the most distinctive form of social capital distinguishing between our high-health and low-health wards.

5. The mere provision of community facilities is not enough to constitute social capital: attention needs to be paid to the processes whereby such facilities are established and run.

Widely accessible council-provided *local facilities* in our high-health ward were minimal, compared to the more extensive council-provided facilities in our low-health community.

However informants in the latter community suggested that these were not as widely used as they might have been. These facilities appeared not to have played the greatest possible role in constituting positive social capital – insofar as community members approached them in the spirit of passive client rather than active participant – and did not see themselves as having any role to play in the design, implementation or regulation of these facilities. If such facilities are to play a positive role in building social capital, merely providing them might not be enough. There needs to be greater participation by, and representation of, ordinary citizens in the conceptualisation and implementation of such facilities.

6. Putnam's conceptualisations of community cohesion, trust and local identity need to be reworked.
Putnam's essentialist conceptualisation of a cohesive civic community bore a greater resemblance to people's romanticised reconstructions of an idealised past than to people's accounts of the complex, fragmented and rapidly changing face of contemporary community life – characterised by relatively high levels of mobility, instability and plurality. Community relationships of local identity and trust existed in a far more restricted form in our communities of interest than Putnam's definition of social capital would suggest. The increasingly plural composition of contemporary communities and the ever-growing rapidity of social change made the possibility of cohesive relationships across unitary communities increasingly unlikely. Contrary to Putnam's inclusive notions of community trust and identity, those relationships of trust and identity that did exist in our wards of interest tended to be restricted to small exclusive face-to-face groups of people (friends, relatives and/or neighbours) who were personally known to one another, and to exclude community residents that fell outside one's personal acquaintance. We have already referred to the large body of sociological literature on the increasingly fragmented nature of local community life in late modern society, resulting in the 'disembedding' or 'dislocation' of the more stable social and community identities of the past (see Chapter 4). Our findings regarding people's perceptions of community, trust and identity were consistent with this literature, and future research should pay more attention to its implications for our understandings of social capital and its implications for health promotion.

7. There are strong within-community differences in the way in which social capital is created, sustained and accessed.
Our research has suggested that social capital is not a homogeneous resource that is equally created, sustained and accessed by all members of a particular community. People are embedded in local networks in different degrees and in different ways. Our data highlighted age-related differences in people's perceptions and experiences of community life. Even more striking were differences in the types of community networks that men and women create and draw on in their day-to-day lives, as well as differences in the types

of support that men and women give and receive from these networks (here the categories 'men' and 'women' need to be used with care – there was also evidence for within-gender variation in relation to networks, for example men's networking and support strategies will vary according to whether they are healthy and single with no responsibilities; married; or single with health problems or family responsibilities). In our particular study gender differences emerged as the most salient source of social capital difference. We hypothesise that differences in social class and ethnicity would also be associated with differences in the types of social capital resources available to different identity groups within a particular community. In particular, we have emphasised the urgent need for health researchers to focus on the impact of socioeconomic status on community networks and relationships. Within-community difference is an aspect of social capital which Putnam's work does not take account of – and one that would have definite implications for those seeking to develop health promotional policies and practices aiming to enhance levels of social capital in local communities.

In this report we have sought to highlight the role that the concept of social capital might play in advancing our understandings of the link between health and community-level networks and relationships. We have illustrated how Putnam's notion of social capital provides a useful starting point for an investigation of the health–community link in local communities in England. We have highlighted seven areas for further conceptual and empirical development of the concept, and believe that, with further clarification and research, the concept could make a important contribution to the development of social and community-level indicators for health promotion.

References

Acheson, D (1998). *Independent inquiry into inequalities in health report*. London: The Stationery Office.

Aggleton, P (1994). *A review of the effectiveness of health education and health promotion*. Amsterdam: Commission of European Communities.

Ajzen, I (1988). *Attitudes, personality and behaviour*. Milton Keynes: Open University Press.

Ankrah, E Maxine (1993). The impact of HIV/AIDS on the family and other significant relationships: the African clan revisited. *AIDS Care* **5**: 5–22.

Antonovsky, A (1984). The sense of coherence as a determinant of health. *Advances* **1**: 37–50.

Antonovsky, A (1987). *Unravelling the mystery of health*. San Francisco: Jossey-Bass.

Asthana, S and Oostvogels, R (1996). Community participation in HIV prevention: problems and prospects for community-based strategies among female sex workers in Madras. *Social Science & Medicine* **43**(2): 133–48.

Bandura, A (1977). Self-efficacy: towards a unifying theory of behavioural change. *Psychological Review* **84**(2): 191–215.

Bandura, A (1986). *Social foundations of thought and action*. Englewood Cliffs, NJ: Prentice Hall.

Bandura, A (1996). *Self-efficacy in changing societies*. Cambridge: Cambridge University Press.

Barnes, M (1997). *Care, communities and citizens*. London: Longman.

Berkman, L (1995). The role of social relations in health promotion. *Psychosomatic Medicine* **57**: 245–54.

Berkman, L and Syme, S (1979). Social networks, host resistance, and mortality: a nine-year follow-up study of Alameida County residents. *American Journal of Epidemiology* **109**(2): 186–204.

Blane, D, Brunner, E and Wilkinson, R (eds) (1996). *Health and social organisation*. London: Routledge.

Blaxter M (1990). *Health and lifestyles*. London: Routledge.

Budlender, D and Dube, N (1998). Starting with what we have: basing development activities on local realities. Johannesburg: Community Agency for Social Enquiry. Unpublished mimeo.

Campbell, C (1998). Peer education and safe sexual behaviour among adolescents. In: Moore, H and Kindness, L (eds) *Promoting the health of children and young people: setting a research agenda*. London: Health Education Authority.

Cohen, S and Syme, L (1984). *Social support and health*. New York: Academic Press.

Crow, G and Allen, G (1994). *Community life: an introduction to local social relations*. Hemel Hempstead: Harvester Wheatsheaf.

Davies, J K and Kelly, M P (eds) (1993). *Healthy Cities: research and practice*. London: Routledge.

Demaine, J and Entwhistle, H (1996) *Beyond communitarianism: citizenship, politics and education*. London: Macmillan.

Department of Environment, Transport and the Regions (1998). *Modern local government*. London: The Stationery Office.

Department of Health (1998a). *Our healthier nation: a contract for health*. London: The Stationery Office.

Department of Health (1998b). *The new NHS: modern, dependable*. London: The Stationery Office.

DiClemente, J (1993a). Preventing HIV/AIDS among adolescents: schools as agents of behaviour change. *Journal of the American Medical Association* **270**(6): 760–2.

DiClemente, R (1993b). Confronting the challenge of AIDS amongst adolescents: directions for future research. *Journal of Adolescent Research* **8**(2): 156–66.

Du Bois-Reymond, M and Ravesloot, J (1994). The role of parents and peers in the sexual and relational socialisation of adolescents. In Nestmann, F and Hurrelman, K (eds). *Social networks and social support in childhood and adolescence*. Berlin: De Gruyter.

Dube, N and Wilson, D (1996). Peer education programmes among HIV-vulnerable communities in southern Africa. In Williams, B and Campbell, C (eds). *HIV/AIDS in the South African mining industry*. Johannesburg: ERU.

Eisen, A (1994). Survey of neighbourhood-based, comprehensive community empowerment initiatives. *Health Education Quarterly* **21**(2): 235–52.

Ell, K (1996). Social networks, social support and coping with serious illness: the family connection. *Social Science & Medicine* **42**(2):173–83.

Eurelings, E, Diekstra, R and Vershuur, M (1995). Psychological distress, social support and social support seeking. *Social Science & Medicine* **40**(8): 1083–9.

Fishbein, M and Ajzen, I (1975). *Belief, attitude, intention and behaviour*. Reading, Massachusetts: Addison-Wesley.

Freire, P (1973). *Education for critical consciousness*. New York: Seabury.

Gatherer, A (1979). *Is health education effective?* London: Health Education Council.

Giddens, A (1990). *The consequences of modernity*. Cambridge: Cambridge University Press.

Gillies, P (1998). The effectiveness of alliances and partnerships for health promotion. *Health Promotion International* **13**: 1–21.

Gillies, P. In Barker, R, Kelly, M, Gillies, P, McVey, D and Morgan, A (1996). Developing social indicators for health promotion: exploratory research. HEA tender document.

Gillies, P and Spray, J (1997). Addressing health inequalities: the practical potential of social capital. London: Health Education Authority. Unpublished mimeo.

Gillies, P, Tolley, K and Wolstenholme, J (1996). Is AIDS a disease of poverty? *AIDS Care* **8**(3): 351–63.

Gottlieb, B (1981). *Social networks and social support*. London: Sage.

Hall, S (1992). The question of cultural identity. In Hall,S, Held,D and McGrew, T (eds). *Modernity and its futures*. Cambridge: Cambridge University Press.

Hancock, T (1993). The healthy city from concept to application. In Davies, J K and Kelly, M P (eds). *Healthy Cities: research and practice*. London: Routledge.

Harriss, J (1997). Missing link or analytically missing: the concept of social capital. *Journal of International Development* **9**(7): 919–37.

Home Office (1998). *Crime and Disorder Act*. London: The Stationery Office.

Israel, B, Checkoway, B, Schulz, A and Zimmerman, M (1994). Health education and community empowerment: conceptualising and measuring perceptions of individual, organisational and community control. *Health Education Quarterly* **21**(2): 149–70.

Janz, N and Becker, M (1984). The Health Belief Model: a decade later. *Health Education Quarterly* **11**: 1–47.

Kelly, J, St Lawrence, J, Diaz, Y, Yvonne Stevenson, L, Hauth, A, Brasfield, T, Kalichman, S, Smith, J and Andrew, M (1991). HIV risk behaviour reduction following intervention with key opinion leaders of population: an experimental analysis. *American Journal of Public Health* **81**(2): 168–71.

Kippax, S and Crawford, J (1993). Flaws in the Theory of Reasoned Action. In Terry, D, Gallois, C and McCamish, M (eds). *The Theory of Reasoned Action: its application to AIDS-preventive behaviour.*. Oxford: Pergamon.

Klein, N, Sondag, A and Drolet, J (1994). Understanding volunteer peer health educators' motivations: applying social learning theory. *Journal of the American College of Health* **43**: 126–31.

Kreuter, M, Lezin, N and Koplan, A (1997). National level assessment of community health promotion using indicators of social capital. Unpublished WHO/EURO working group report. Atlanta, Georgia: Centers for Disease Control.

Labonte, R (1994). Health promotion and empowerment: reflections on professional practice. *Health Education Quarterly* **21**(2): 253–68.

Leonardi, R (1997). A review of the literature on social capital. Interim report to the Health Education Authority. London: Health Education Authority (unpublished).

Leonardi, R, Wood, R, Penn, G, Morgan, A and Walters, R (in preparation). *Social capital and health – a pilot survey* .

Levi, M (1996). Social and unsocial capital: a review essay of Putnam's *Making democracy work*. *Politics and Society* **24**(1): 45–55.

Lomas, J (1998). Social capital and health: implications for public health and epidemiology. *Social Science & Medicine* **47**(9): 1181–8.

Lunt, P and Livingstone, S (1996). Rethinking the focus group in media and communications research. *Journal of Communication* **46**(2): 79–98.

Macintyre, S and Ellaway, A (1996). Social and local variations in the use of urban neighbourhoods: a case study in Glasgow. Unpublished mimeo. Glasgow: Medical Research Council.

Macintyre, S, Maciver, S and Sooman, A (1993). Area, class or health: should we be focusing on places or people? *Journal of Social Policy* **22**(2): 213–34.

Madan, T (1987). Community involvement in health policy: socio-structural and dynamic aspects of health beliefs. *Social Science & Medicine* **25**(6): 615–20.

Marmot, M, Rose, G, Shipley, M and Hamilton, P (1975). Employment grade and coronary heart disease in British civil servants. *Journal of Epidemiology and Community Health* **3**: 244–9.

Marsh, A and McKay, S (1994). *Poor smokers.* London: Policy Studies Institute.

Mellanby, A, Phelps, F, Crichton, N and Tripp, J (1995). School sex education: an experimental programme with educational and medical benefit. *British Medical Journal* **311**: 414–17.

Milburn, K (1995). A critical review of peer education with young people with special reference to sexual health. *Health education research: theory and practice* **10**(4): 407–20.

Morrow, V (in preparation). Conceptualising social capital in relation to the well-being of children and young people. *The Sociological Review.*

Narayan, D and Pritchett, L (1997). *Cents and sociability: household income and social capital in rural Tanzania.* World Bank Social Development Policy Research Working Paper, No. 1796 (unpublished).

National AIDS Trust (1995). Shared responsibilities. London: NAT.

Ogden, J (1996). *Health psychology.* Buckingham: Open University Press.

Pahl, R (1995). Friendly society. *New Statesman and Society*, 10 March.

Pahl, Ray (1996). Friendly society. In Kraemer, S and Roberts, J (eds). *The politics of attachment: towards a secure society.* London: Free Association Books.

Perri 6 (1997). *Escaping poverty: from safety networks to networks of opportunity.* London: Demos.

Popay, J, Williams, G, Thomas, C and Gatrell, T (1998). Theorising inequalities in health: the place of lay knowledge. *Sociology of Health and Illness* **20**(5): 619–44.

Prochaska, J, Redding, C, Harlow, L and Rossi, J (1994). The transtheoretical model of change and HIV prevention: a review. *Health Education Quarterly* **21**(4): 471–86.

Portes, A (1998). Social capital: its origins and applications in modern sociology. *Annual Review of Sociology* **24**:1–24.

Putnam, R (1993a). *Making democracy work: civic traditions in modern Italy.* New Jersey: Princeton University Press.

Putnam, R (1993b). The prosperous community: social capital and public life. *American Prospect* **13**: 35–42.

Putnam, R (1995). Bowling alone: America's declining social capital. *Journal of Democracy* **6** (1): 65–79.

Rhodes, T (1994a). HIV outreach, peer education and community change: developments and dilemmas. *Health Education Journal* **53**: 92–9.

Rhodes, T (1994b). Outreach, community change and community empowerment: contradictions for public health and health promotion. In Aggleton, P (1994). *AIDS: foundations for the future.* London: Falmer Press.

Rissel, C (1994). Empowerment: the holy grail of health promotion? *Health Promotion International* **9** (1): 39–45.

Rogers, E M (1983). *Diffusion of innovations.* New York: Free Press.

Rose, G (1992). *The strategy of preventive medicine.* Oxford: Oxford University Press.

Sapolsky, R (1993). Endocrinology alfresco: psychoendocrine studies of wild baboons. *Recent Progress in Hormone Research* **48**: 437–68.

Schoepf, B (1993). AIDS action research in women in Kinshasa, Zaire. *Social Science & Medicine* **37** (11): 1401–13.

Schulz, A (1995). Empowerment as a multi-level construct: perceived control at the individual, organisational and community levels. *Health Education Research: Theory and Practice* **10** (3) 309–27.

Social Exclusion Unit (1998). *Bringing Britain together: a national strategy for neighbourhood renewal.* London: The Stationery Office.

Stockdale, J. (1995). The self and media messages: match or mismatch? In Markova, I. and Farr, R. (eds). *Representations of health, illness and handicap.* Chur, Switzerland: Harwood Academic.

Stockdale, J, Dockrell, J and Wells, A (1989). The self in relation to mass media representations of HIV and AIDS. *Health Education Journal* **48** (3): 121–30.

Stone, L (1992). Cultural influences in community participation in health. *Social Science & Medicine* **35** (4): 409–17.

Strickland, B (1978). Internal–external expectancies and health-related behaviours. *Journal of Consulting and Clinical Psychology* **46**: 1192–1211.

Stroebe, W and Stroebe, M (1995). *Social psychology and health*. Buckingham: Open University Press.

Tawil, O, Verster, A and O'Reilly, K (1995). Enabling approaches for HIV/AIDS promotion: can we modify the environment and minimise the risk? *AIDS* **9**: 1299–1306.

Tsouros, A (ed.) (1990). *WHO Healthy Cities Project: a project becomes a movement (review of progress 1987 to 1990)*. Copenhagen: WHO/FADL.

Wiist, W and Snider, G (1991). Peer education in friendship cliques: prevention of adolescent smoking. *Health Education Research* **6** (1): 101–8.

Wilkinson, R (1996). *Unhealthy societies: the afflictions of inequality*. London: Routledge.

Wilton, T and Aggleton, P (1991). Condoms, coercion and control: heterosexuality and the limits to HIV/AIDS education. In Aggleton, P, Hart, G and Davies, P (eds). *AIDS: responses, interventions and care*. London: Falmer Press.

Appendices

Appendix A. In-depth interview informants

Farley – Women

Interview	Age	Marital status	Ethnic origin	Employment	No. in house	Children	Years in ward
Info 2	33	Divorced	White	Unemployed/HW	4	3	7
Info 4	36	Single	White	Unemployed/HW	4	3	36
Info 7	76	Widowed	White	Retired	2	(2)	50+
Info 8	78	Widowed	White	Retired	1	(2)	45
Info 16	66	Married	White	Retired	2	(2)	43+
Info 21	33	Married	White	Security officer	5	3	4
Info 22	50	Married	White	Teacher	5	5	10
Info 23	34	Single	White	Unemployed/HW	2	1	4
Info 24	65	Married	White	Retired	2	(2)	15
Info 30	39	Married	White	Dinner lady	5	(3)	10

Farley – Men

Interview	Age	Marital status	Ethnic origin	Employment	No. in house	Children	Years in ward
Info 1	61	Married	White	Retired/sick	2	(4)	21
Info 5	46	Married	White	Train driver	6	3	6
Info 9	46	Married	White	Assembly worker	2	(1 + 4)	15
Info 12	16	Single	White	Student	7	6	1
Info 28	50	Divorced	White	Sick	3	1 (3)	25
Info 29	52	Married	White	Unemploy/sick	3	1	7
Info 31	17	Single	White	Student	3	1	16
Info 32	78	Widowed	White	Retired	1	(1)	35+

Sundon Park – Women

Interview	Age	Marital status	Ethnic origin	Employment	No. in house	Children	Years in ward
Info 3	50	Married	White	Unemployed/HW	3	1	24
Info 6	35	Married	White	PT florist	4	2	9
Info 10	65	Married	White	Unemployed/HW	2	(3)	40+
Info 17	56	Married	White	Retired	2	(1)	32
Info 27	32	Married	White	Unemployed/HW	5	3	6.5
Info 33	16	Single	White	Student	4	2	16
Info 34	31	Married	White	PT distributor	5	3	12
Info 40	45	Married	White	Financial	2	0	45

Sundon Park – Men

Interview	Age	Marital status	Ethnic origin	Employment	No. in house	Children	Years in ward
Info 11	30	Single	African-Caribbean	Unemployed	1	(1)	24
Info 13	69	Widower	White	Retired	1	(3)	9
Info 14	42	Cohabit	White	Carer	3	1	40+
Info 15	76	Divorced	White	Retired	1	(2)	32
Info 25	75	Married	White	Retired	2	(2)	6.5
Info 26	53	Widowed	White	Stoker	2	(1+2)	16
Info 35	62	Married	White	Retired	2	0	12
Info 36	70	Married	White	Retired	2	(1)	17
Info 37	17	Single	White	Student	3	1	45
Info 38	17	Single	White	Fork engineer	3	(1)	3.5
Info 39	39	Married	White	Joiner	5	2	8

Appendix B. Interview topic guide

Introduction to three-hour interview

I am a researcher from the London School of Economics/Health Education Authority with a particular interest in health promotion. Recently it has been suggested that one way to keep people healthy is through developing cohesive and supportive local communities where people trust one another, help one another out, and where people are concerned about the community as a whole, rather than just about themselves and their own immediate families.

Such a community is said to improve health in two ways. Firstly if you live in such a community you have a circle of people who will help you or your family members when you get sick or have an accident. But secondly – if you live in such a community you are less likely to suffer the damaging effects of the stresses and strains of daily life – which are also very bad for our health in the long term.

So this is the area that we are looking at in our research – we are looking at a number of communities where levels of health are good and bad – and we want to see if there are any differences in the extent to which these different communities are supportive – to what extent do people in the different areas trust one another, to what extent do they stick to themselves, or to what extent do they tend to be sociable. To what extent do people belong to organisations such as the church or to sports clubs – or to what extent do people stay at home and watch TV with their own kids.

So today I would like to ask you lots of questions – the interview takes three hours – and I will start off by asking you about your life history. After that I will be going through some of the questions that our survey team asked you [in the parallel Leonardi study through which we recruited informants] to get information about why you gave particular answers to particular questions.

As you will see, the questions are very easy – and there are no right or wrong answers. What we are interested in are your own personal opinions. Before we start the interviews I will need to get you to sign a consent form. As researchers we operate under a strict codes of ethics – and as such we cannot interview people unless we have their signed consent. The consent form specifies a number of things:

1. Firstly you must confirm that the aims of the study have been explained to you, and

that you are willing to participate.

2. That any information you give us will be completely confidential – the tape recording will be typed out by a secretary – and then no one will have access to the interview transcript apart from members of our six-person research team.

3. In our final research report the information you give us will be presented in such a way that no one can identify you – your participation in the study is anonymous.

4. If at any stage of the interview you decide you don't want to participate any more, you are free to say so.

5. You need to agree that you are happy for the interview to be tape recorded.

If all goes according to plan the interview should take three hours, and we will pay you £15 for your participation.

Are there any questions you want to ask about the study before signing the consent form?

Developing community indicators for health promotion: life history interviews

Aim to get people to talk about things in relation to their own experience and life history, rather than to make vague generalisations. Wherever possible, try and pin generalisations down to relate to particular people, places or situations that relate to the informant personally.

Please tell us the story of your life from the beginning. (Preferable to let people do this in their own way – and then go through the checklist of items below afterwards to check that all has been covered. If people cannot do this, you can go through the topic guide item by item. If people seem to 'go off the point' this is often good rather than bad (within reason of course – since we have to finish within the time available.)

- *Birth* – where, circumstances (both parents around, how many other children in the family etc.)?
- *Parents* – what were they like, what sort of relationship did they have with one another, what kind of people were they (education, social class, ethnicity, place of origin, employment), what sort of relationship did parents have with informants?
- *Extended family* (grandparents, aunts, etc.) – what role did these play in informant's upbringing?
- *Community they grew up in* – what was it like? [*If they grew up in another place*] In what way was the community you grew up in different from Farley/Sundon Park? [*If they grew up in the same place*] How was the community different in your childhood compared to how it is now? Were things 'better' or 'worse' for you then? What do you

mean by 'better' or 'worse'? How was their family's relationships with neighbours?

- *School* – did they enjoy school, what kind of school did they go to, in what ways were things different for schoolkids then compared to now, how did they do at school (i.e. academically, interpersonally, leadershipwise, etc.)?
- *Peer group* – what sort of friends did you have as a child (0–10), as a teenager (11–20)?
- *Formative influences* – what were the most important people/events influencing your early childhood (0–10), your teenage years?
- *Voluntary associations* – as a child, did your parents/family members belong to any? Which of these do they remember playing an important role in the life of the community when they were growing up? (prompting examples: church, PTAs etc., clubs or societies of any sort)
- *Educational history*
- *Employment history*
- *Relationships (emotional/sexual)* – What is your relationship history? *Marriage*(s)? *Cohabitation*(s)? *Children*? Details of all these.
- *Health history*: Can you tell us the history of your health?
- *Physical health* – childhood, teenager, adulthood. [*With regard to good health*] How is it that you have kept so healthy? [*With regard to each health problem raised*] How did you deal with this problem? What support did you get from the state? From the community? From friends? From family? From organisations? From others?
- *Mental/emotional health* [*support questions as above*]
- *Social health* – to what extent have you had access to the resources that you have needed to do what you want in life – education, employment, money?
- *General sense of wellbeing* – would you describe yourself as a happy person? If so, why? If not, why not?

What do people consider as their 'community'?
Which sentence says the most about you:
- I live in England/Britain.
- I live in Luton.
- I live in Farley/Sundon Park.
- Why have you chosen this sentence? [*probe*]

More specific social capital questions

Go through Leonardi's questionnaire (46 questions). Ask them to give reasons for each answer. Here it is important to make clear that the questions refer to Farley or Sundon Park. If informants feel that these are not useful categories, get them to say why in each case.

'Empowerment' questions

- *Self-efficacy* – If you look back on your life, to what extent do you feel that you have been in control of decisions, events that mattered to you, or to what extent do you feel you have been a victim of forces outside your control? [*might have to bring in specific examples from their life history – but it would be preferable for informants to interpret the question as they wish*]
- *Social support* – Speaking generally, to what extent do you feel that you have had support from friends, neighbours, people within the Farley/Sundon Park community when you have had particular problems/challenges in your life [*by now you should be able to highlight what the person's central life challenges/problems have been from the life history etc.*] – or to what extent have you dealt with them alone, or in the context of immediate family?
- *Social networks*
- *Relative power and status within organisations* [*If the person has ever worked or been involved in any organisational or institutional context involving hierarchy*] In this situation did you ever have any feelings about being part of a hierarchy? Admiration or resentment towards people 'above' you or 'below' you?
- *Perceptions of relative deprivation* – To what extent do you feel that you have had a good deal in life – or to what extent do you feel that you have been a victim of social inequality?
- The hypothesis of our project is that community cohesion, trust, mutual help and support, and involvement in community activities enhances people's health. Does this make sense to you? In what way?

Appendix C. NUD*ST coding frame: categories for analysis of in-depth interviews

1 OLD DAYS (informants' accounts of social capital in 'the old days')
   1.1 NOW v. THEN (direct comparisons of past and present)

2 ASSOCIATIONAL LIFE (references to parents' networks and group membership)
   2.1 FATHER'S (father's networks)
   2.2 MOTHER'S (mother's networks)
   2.3 SELF (informant's network as a child or in the past)

3 NETWORKS (description of types of networks that exist in the community)
   3.1 INFORMAL (general informal networks)
        3.1.1   NEIGHBOUR'S (role of neighbours as community network)
        3.1.2   FRIENDS (role of friends as informal community network)
        3.1.3   FAMILY (role of family as informal community network)
        3.1.3.1 CHILDREN (role of children in accessing informal networks)
        3.1.4   EMPLOYMENT (role of employment as social network)
        3.1.5   GENDER DIFFERENCES (role of gender in networks)
   3.2 VOLUNTARY GROUPS (voluntary groupings that exist in the community)
        3.2.1   CHURCH
        3.2.2   SCOUTS, GUIDES, ETC.
        3.2.3   WOMEN'S GROUPS
        3.2.4   SPORTS GROUPS
        3.2 5   CHILD-RELATED GROUPS
        3.2.3   TRADE UNIONS AND POLITICAL GROUPS
        3.2.4   RESIDENTS' ASSOCIATIONS ETC.
        3.2.5   VOLUNTARY WORK
   3.3 FORMAL (formal community networks linked to local government)
        3.3.1   COMMUNITY FACILITIES (community centres, cafés, leisure centres, etc).
        3.3.1.1 OPEN SPACES (parks and other open spaces)
        3.3.1.2 SHOPS (shops and outside shops as places where people meet)

4 SUPPORT (forms of social support)
   4.1 ADVICE (what relationships exist to give people advice in general)
   4.2 BORROW (borrowing things from others, e.g. food, equipment, etc.)
   4.3 ILLNESS (sources of support and help in times of illness)
   4.4 COMPANION (sources of companionship for people)
   4.5 CHILD CARE (people helping with child care)
   4.6 EMOTIONAL (emotional support in times of bereavement, divorce, etc.)
   4.7 FORMAL (formal support systems, e.g. health or social services)
   4.8 PRACTICAL (any other kind of practical assistance, e.g. gardening, car, etc.)

5 ACCESSING (issues around accessing support networks)
   5.1 INFORMAL (issues around accessing informal networks)
   5.2 FORMAL (issues around accessing formal networks)

6 COMMUNITY ACTION (any kind of personal or local community action)
   6.1 SUCCEED (examples of when community action succeeded and why)
   6.2 FAIL (examples of when community action failed and why)
   6.3 VOTE (voting as a channel for bringing about community action)

7.1–7.46 SURVEY (categories of informants' answers to survey questions)

8 CON COMMUNITY (informants' conceptualisation of their community)
   8.1 SAFETY (extent to which informant feels safe in the community)
   8.2 CONFLICT (forms and sources of conflict in the community)
   8.3 YOUTH (role of young people in the community)
   8.4 BUILD (informants' view on how to build community)
   8.5 OLD (anything about the role of old people in the community)
   8.6 GENDER (anything about gender and the community)
   8.7 PLEASANT (reference to attractive features etc.)
   8.8 LONGEVITY (anything about people and continuity etc.)
   8.9 OWNERSHIP (being part of or taking responsibility for local area)
   8.10 POLITICS (anything about the role of politics in everyday life)

9 COMMUNITY (descriptions of local community)
   9.1 STRENGTHS (positive features of the community)
   9.2 WEAKNESSES (disadvantages, lacks in the community)

10 HEALTH (reference to individual health status or general health references)
   10.1 LIFE SATISFACTION (are people happy and satisfied with life?)
   10.2 CLASS (people's perceptions of social class)
   10.3 HEALTH PROMOTION (informants' views on how to promote health)

10.4   PERCEPTIONS OF HEALTH (what constitutes, promotes or hinders health)

10.5   GENDER DIFFERENCES (in health, perception of, use of health service, etc.)

10.5.1. STRESS AND COPING (gender differences, stress and coping)

10.6   SOCIAL HEALTH (unemployment, poverty, poor housing, social problems, etc.)

10.7   MENTAL HEALTH (any reference to anxiety, depression, addiction or distress)

11 EVENTS (specific events in the community, e.g. carnivals, fetes, etc.)

12 FEEDBACK (people's perceptions of our study and the experience of being interviewed)